THE *Natural History* OF THE Southwest

DESERT SUNSET. The traveler to the Southwest takes home with him many impressions, not the least of which would be this silhouetted cactus against the sunset sky near Tucson, Arizona. *American Airlines*

THE *Natural History* OF THE SOUTHWEST

EDITED BY

WILLIAM A. BURNS

Editor, Man and Nature Publications
The American Museum of Natural History

CONTRIBUTING EDITORS

WILLIAM H. WOODIN
Director

MERWIN W. LARSON
Curator of Exhibits

LEWIS WAYNE WALKER
Associate Curator

PEGGY PICKERING LARSON
Staff Associate

OF THE ARIZONA-SONORA DESERT MUSEUM

FRANKLIN WATTS, INC.
575 LexingtonAvenue • New York 22

Designed & Produced by
George McKibbin, New York

Library of Congress Catalog Card Number: 59-7072

Printed in the United States of America
by the Polygraphic Company of America, Inc.

FIRST PRINTING

Table of Contents

PINNACLE BALANCED ROCK, Chiricahua National Monument. An immense lava boulder has been weathered so that it stands on a relatively narrow neck, yet probably will withstand the elements for thousands of years before it falls. *Southern Pacific Company*

PETROGLYPH of mountain lion standing before the headquarters of the Petrified Forest National Monument, Arizona. *National Park Service*

The Story of the Southwest

BY WILLIAM A. BURNS

THE SOUTHWEST is a region of the United States of America. It is also a state of mind, both to the people who live there and to those who may or may not have visited this ancient and spectacular land. It is a land of contrasts, of clear and crystal distances where a tenderfoot may set out for a mountain that seems to lie across the first ridge and actually is fifty miles away. It is a land where a gullied dry stream bed may suddenly turn into a brown and frothing torrent of mud and water, to sweep away the unwary and unfamiliar camper. It is a country of farming without water and of farming with water transported through the arid desert for many miles to nourish the roots of lettuce, succulent canteloupe, or cotton. It is the home of ancient Indian peoples whose ancestors once hunted the mammoth and the giant sloth. Its speech is a combination of the soft, slurred Spanish of the conquistadores; the sometimes sharp, clipped staccato of the Pueblo Indians; the easy drawl of the native Anglo-American. It boasts gleaming white modern cities and the cliff-perched homes of aborigines long gone from the scene.

It is an old land and a new land – old in its prehistory, history, and traditions, and new politically. Its states are among the latest to become part of the Union and its rich resources have enabled it to build some of the best-planned and most up-to-date municipalities in the nation. Yet it is still spacious, with plenty of room in which to move and to breathe and to expand. With the newly-found wealth from oil and cattle and crops, it attracts

FROM THE NORTH RIM of the Grand Canyon, Grand Canyon National Park, Arizona. The Grand Canyon is one of the world's stupendous spectacles. *Union Pacific Railroad Photo*

culture in the form of colleges, universities, and museums whose collections may one day rival those of the East.

It is a region proud of its brawling beginnings. Its heroes do not become proficient in kissing ladies' hands. Rather do they ride through the lurid pages of its early history, shooting, roping, branding, fighting, with the smell of sweat and leather and gunpowder and oil and cattle strong in their nostrils. The Southwest had no need for Paul Bunyans or John Henrys. It had its Sam Houstons, its Jim Bowies, its Davy Crocketts, its Buffalo Bills in every county — real men repeating the exploits of real men, time and time again.

It repeated the darker aspects of its northern and western neighbors, too. It had its own bloody massacres of Indians; its own land grabs; its internal wars against settlers who preferred to raise sheep instead of cattle; its banishing of the original inhabitants to reservations where many of them still live; and its bad men and their bloody exploits, without which television would lack much good material.

The region which is called the Southwest is a natural geographical division lying south of the Rocky Mountains; it is drained by the upper Rio Grande and its tributary, the Pecos, and by the Colorado River and its three eastern branches, the San Juan, the Little Colorado, and the Gila. It includes the entire states of Arizona and New Mexico, embraces western Texas, southern Utah, southern Colorado, western Oklahoma, and southeastern Nevada.

Arizona, the sixth largest state in the Union, is

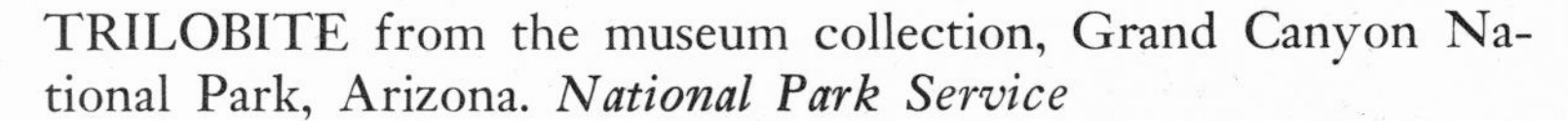
TRILOBITE from the museum collection, Grand Canyon National Park, Arizona. *National Park Service*

BRIGHT ANGEL CANYON, Grand Canyon National Park. The mighty and ancient formations of the Grand Canyon never fail to awe the visitor. Some of its formations are over 1,500,000,000 years old. *Natt N. Dodge, National Park Service*

FOSSIL IMPRESSIONS OF LEAVES found in shale in the Petrified Forest National Park, Arizona. *National Park Service*

divided into three distinct geographical areas. In the north are high plateaus cut into by deep canyons; in the middle part of the state are high mountain ranges; in the south is the huge desert crossed by the Gila River in the west and low river plains in the east.

In the north is the remarkable Grand Canyon of the Colorado River. The history of this magnificent formation is the history of the earth itself. A study of its rocks reveals that some are 1,500,000,000 years old. Going up in time, the prehistorian can trace various great periods in earth history — the Archean, the Paleozoic, the Devonian, the Mesozoic — and some of its rocks contain fossil creatures from earliest times.

Water, wind, and temperature have worn the walls and carved the mighty formations of the Grand Canyon. To come upon it unexpectedly is to stand stupefied at its enormous depths; to gasp at its colors that change with every cloud that passes over it or with every movement of the sun from dawn to dusk; to mark with awe and wonder its spires, battlements, buttes, mesas, arches, caves, precipices, slopes, towers, and cliffs.

Almost as colorful as the Grand Canyon, but not as awe-inspiring, is the Painted Desert extending along the northeast bank of the Little Colorado River from the Grand Canyon to the Petrified Forest. This kaleidoscopic desert, called "Painted" because of the brilliant yellows, reds, magentas, and purples of its sands and rocks, rises in terraces, mesas, and hills for three hundred miles.

Like the Grand Canyon, the Painted Desert changes its colors with changes in its temperature and the intensity of its light. Even its dust-devils whirl in lilac or yellow clouds that turn, as you watch, to blue, to amethyst, and to blood red.

The Petrified Forest National Monument was created for perhaps two reasons: first, because such a phenomenon is worth the notice of the government; and second, because, had it not been protected, tourists and commercial interests might have removed the petrified trees in their entirety for curios and ornaments.

About a hundred and fifty million years ago the area now known as the Petrified Forest was part of a great valley. Deposits of silt and sand filled the valley and covered the trees to a depth of almost three thousand feet. Minerals dissolved in the ground water seeped into the tree trunks, replacing the wood cells with stone. Now water erosion has uncovered much of the forest as it is seen today.

New Mexico has no Grand Canyon but its rocks are fully as old, if not older, than those found in the Canyon. It is estimated that some of the New Mexican formations are from one to two billions of years old. Instead of climbing down to study these formations, the visitor climbs up mountain ranges where every period of the geological time table is represented.

New Mexico is noted for its natural caves, particularly the Carlsbad Cavern National Park. This enormous hole in the ground has a constant temperature of 56° F. both in winter and summer. The cavern was made in limestone rock by the action of water, and its intricate and decorative deposits were left by limestone-bearing solutions that dripped and evaporated, leaving the minerals be-

PETRIFIED WOOD in polished cross-sections, from the Museum collection at Petrified Forest National Monument, Arizona. *National Park Service*

DEATH VALLEY, View from Zabriskie Point. Although the temperatures of Death Valley are deadly in the summer, it is a pleasant winter resort. *Union Pacific Railroad Colorphoto*

DELICATE ARCH, with snow-capped La Sal Mountains in background, Arches National Monument, Utah. *National Park Service*

hind. Stalactites were formed from seepages above, leaving the characteristic "icicles" depending from the ceiling. Stalagmites rose from the dripping of mineral-bearing solutions from the ceiling to the floor. Sometimes the stalactites and the stalagmites meet, forming columns. Minute quantities of iron or other elements or compounds in the solutions give the formations their beautiful colors. From three to five million bats live in the cavern and emerge every evening in huge flights, to return after a night's foraging for food. Hundreds of thousands of tons of bat guano have been taken from the cavern, to be employed in the manufacture of fertilizer.

Every year many thousands of people visit other southwestern features of note, among them Shiprock, the Zuñi Salt Crater, the Enchanted Mesa, White Sands National Monument, and Inscription Rock.

It is difficult to believe, after one has been through Colorado, that it was once wholly or partially submerged by arms of the sea and at least four times was at the bottom of an ocean. All of this happened about half a billion years ago; and since then many gradual changes have pushed up the jagged granite and sedimentary layers into what are now known as the Rocky Mountains.

Paleontologists find the rocks of Colorado a bone-hunter's paradise. The remains of the great prehistoric reptiles are plentiful and, after their

NATURAL BRIDGE, Capitol Reef National Monument, Utah. This is Hickman Natural Bridge, formed by erosion of wind and water. *National Park Service*

demise, prehistoric mammals left their bones in more recent rocks. Only a short time ago paleontologists from The American Museum of Natural History unearthed the first uncrushed skulls of little eohippus, the "dawn horse" or ancestor of our modern horse, in southern Colorado.

High on the cliffs of southern Colorado may be seen the dwelling places of peoples who climbed to make their homes safe from enemies. Among the most famous are those of Mesa Verde National Park, containing more than 350 cliff homes and 400 mesa pueblos. Many have been excavated, and visitors may see in what manner the original inhabitants lived.

The greater part of Utah belongs to what is commonly called the "West," but the southern part belongs to the Southwest. At its southeastern corner it meets the states of Colorado, Arizona, and New Mexico and this area is a huge triangular plateau, deeply cut into canyons and gorges, strewn with fantastic shapes in eroded sandstone. Tourists are coming in ever-increasing numbers to see such places as Capitol Reef, Natural Bridge, Arches, and Rainbow Bridge national monuments. In the south central part of the state are Zion and Bryce canyons, both national parks, rivaling the Grand Canyon of the Colorado, if not in size and grandeur, at least in diversity of color and strangely shaped formations.

Southeastern Nevada may properly be included

"BIG ROOM," Carlsbad Caverns National Park, southeastern New Mexico. The limestone caverns are said to be more than 60 million years in the making. *New Mexico State Tourist Bureau*

in the Southwest since it touches on Utah and northern Arizona. Like the other states in the Southwest, it offers evidence of primitive human beings who lived perhaps 10,000 years ago. So far back do the earliest human remains go that they were found in company with the remains of long-extinct ground sloths.

One of the great settlements found in southeastern Nevada is Pueblo Grande de Nevada, Lost City. Thousands of pieces of pottery, jewelry, baskets, textiles, stone and bone tools, and shell beads were found here. This settlement doubtless existed between 600 and 900 A.D.

The second largest state in the Union, Texas, is fabulous. The visitor is impressed with its almost limitless spaces. The Central Plains and the Western High Plains are like vast oceans. On these great plains the bison was replaced by large herds of longhorn steers that were moved by the millions along the famed Chisholm Trail overland to railway shipping points. The names of men who came to these shipping points to relax with a pocketful of money and a few days in town are synonymous with reckless daring, cool nerve, and sometimes the ability to get out of town in a hurry. Texas was rich in cattle and in 1901, with the discovery of oil in Beaumont, the great state entered a new era: the era of oil.

Oil changed much of the face of Texas. Where cattle once grazed, derricks now push into the sky

CARLSBAD CAVERN, New Mexico. Underground water has carved out and ornamented the beautiful chambers in the Carlsbad Cavern. Stalactites ("c" for ceiling) and stalagmites ("g" for ground) sometimes meet to form columns. *Ray Manley, American Airlines*

THE GIANT DOME in Carlsbad Caverns National Park, New Mexico. 37 miles of the caverns have been explored but no one knows how far they extend under the Guadalupe Mountains. *New Mexico State Tourist Bureau*

SHIPROCK towers 1,640 feet above the plains. This great formation, sacred to the Indians, may be seen in the heart of New Mexico's Navajo Indian Reservation. *New Mexico State Tourist Bureau*

like a forest of steel. Pipelines were laid and tank farms built. Refineries came into being and the rich product of Texas supplied one-fourth of the world's demands for oil. With oil came fabulous wealth and some of it was diverted into needed irrigation projects so that the fertile but arid desert lands could produce much of the food for the nation's tables.

As was suggested before, culture commonly follows wealth and the Southwest, with its great fortunes, may well become one of the world's important centers for great art treasures. A good start has been made in what are becoming some of the nation's leading museums.

Oklahoma, like Texas, is a rich oil state. It offers great diversity to the visitor in its wide, treeless plains in the west and its heavily-wooded mountains in the east. Like other southwestern states, its plains have been carved into many canyons, mesas, and arroyos by the cutting action of wind and water.

Like Texas too, Oklahoma has always been cat-

CAPITOL REEF NATIONAL MONUMENT, Utah. Erosion and imagination produced The Castle. Note the foreground erosion patterns. *Union Pacific Railroad Colorphoto*

tle country. Oil has enriched the state, and its mineral deposits of zinc, lead, coal, and gypsum are still enormous.

The earliest inhabitants of the region known as the Southwest are known only by the artifacts they left behind. Fortunately the nature of the southwestern climate is such that dryness and comparatively little rainfall have preserved much material that otherwise would have been lost.

Nothing is known of the language of these ancient people. We know little or nothing of their religious beliefs except that many of the artifacts found in their ruins must have had some religious use. We know that after they came to the Southwest they experienced various cultural changes that may be inferred from a study of the sites where they lived.

Apparently the Southwest was a dry land when the Ancients lived there, as it is today. They settled at the highest points of the country, where they could benefit from the greatest rainfall, or they lived in the river valleys where water could be obtained for irrigation.

When the Spanish arrived, the written history of the peoples of the Southwest began. Only the archaeologist can determine the way of life of the peoples before that time. We know that there were two main periods in which they were found: the period of the Basket Makers and that of the Pueblo Builders.

The earliest known form of culture of the Southwest is that of the Basket Makers. At its beginnings the peoples must have led a nomadic life and known little or nothing about agriculture; and they left few remains. They used spear-throwers instead of bows and arrows, wore skin clothing, and built no permanent dwellings.

Various periods indicating the development of the Basket Makers included the growth of such skills as the weaving of baskets, footgear, and bags; the fashioning of the first true pottery; and the raising of beans and maize.

The Pueblo people added the building of permanent stone houses; the rise of the small village; the great period during which large settlements were built; the contact with the first white explorers

SAND DUNES OF PURE GYPSUM rippled by the wind. White Sands National Monument, New Mexico. *National Park Service*

GRAND CANYON NATIONAL PARK, Arizona. The great majesty of the Grand Canyon, with its deep chasms and isolated peaks, moves some to awed silence and some to actual tears. *National Park Service*

RIM OF THE PAINTED DESERT. The Painted Desert's mystery and charm lie in its ever-changing colors that turn from blood-red to lilac to purple as you watch. *National Park Service*

CAPITOL REEF NATIONAL MONUMENT, Utah. The effects of wind, rain, heat, cold, and frost erosion sometimes produce strange formations. This one is called the Watchman. *Union Pacific Railroad Colorphoto*

SANTA CLARA PUEBLO INDIANS, New Mexico, performing the Deer Dance, a winter ritual. The dancers wear antlers and carry a staff to represent the front legs. *New Mexico State Tourist Bureau*

and settlers, the Spaniards; and the Pueblo period, from the Spanish conquest to the present time.

Even if most people have never heard of the Basket Makers, almost everybody knows something about the Pueblo Indians. Their wonderful ancient buildings, perched many hundreds of feet high against a canyon overhang, their colorful pottery, their fine weaving and silverwork, and their tribal dances are familiar to all who have visited the Southwest or who have read about it.

The old Pueblo houses were usually located in positions relatively easy to defend from enemies. Caves, overhanging cliffs, or even valley floors provided easily protected sites. They were usually built in the form of a square or a rectangle or sometimes in a semicircle around an open central court. They were terraced back to form a strong, high wall with no windows low enough to permit a foe to creep in.

To make their homes, the people used the materials that were easily picked up around them. If they could locate soft sandstone that would cut easily, they made their homes of sandstone blocks or pieces. They used solidified volcanic ash or tufa or they picked up round river boulders that were light enough to handle easily. They also used clay mortar and later found out, from the Spanish, how to bake adobe bricks in the hot southwestern sun.

Many a modern house in the Southwest is made

THE BASKET DANCE, performed by San Juan Pueblo (New Mexico) Indians wearing willow and feather headdresses. *New Mexico State Tourist Bureau*

almost in the same manner as those constructed by the Pueblo Indians long years ago. The walls are a combination of stonework and adobe brick, and the clay for the bricks may come from the back yard of the owner. Ceilings are made of crossed logs, filled in with small poles, layers of sticks and brush, and a final thick coating of wet clay. The walls are still whitewashed or plastered and sometimes ornamented in colored bands.

These modern houses differ only from the ancient Pueblo Indian houses in that they are more than likely to be fitted with windows and doors of modern manufacture. The Pueblo Indian made small windows in his house, and his doors were more like French windows through which he could step from the ladder that led to his level. The higher "apartments" were reached by ladders, and lower stories sometimes were made with hatchways. When the ladders were drawn up, the community was secured against attack.

One of the largest and best known of the cliff-dwellings is Cliff Palace on Mesa Verde, Colorado. It is in a huge cave that is 425 feet long, 80 feet wide, and 80 feet high. The depth of the Cliff Palace Canyon is about 200 feet. In one building alone there are 117 rooms. It seems that the first buildings were enlarged by the construction of newer additions from time to time. Evenly-cut sandstone blocks laid with adobe mortar make up the structure of the newer rooms. A yellow mud plaster was applied on the inside and on part of the outside walls and was smoothed out with the hands; finger marks are still plain to see.

Many of the rooms are equipped with fireplaces and the walls are black with smoke since there were no chimneys. Other rooms without windows were doubtless used to store food. There are 23 kivas in the courtyard of Cliff Palace. Kivas are rooms, usually built in a circular shape, below ground, and used for ceremonial purposes. Today's kivas have changed but little and are sacred rooms, but they are also used for meeting places and workshops.

Pueblo Bonito, in Chaco Canyon, dwarfs Cliff Palace since it is 667 feet long and 315 feet wide and was originally four or five stories high. This great community house contained more than five hundred rooms.

The Pueblo Indians were agriculturalists. They grew maize or Indian corn, beans, and squash. They turned the soil with simple wooden or horn tools. If there was not enough moisture in the ground or the rainfall was lacking, they dug irrigation ditches and directed the water of rivers and creeks to the fields in which crops were in need of water. So well planned were some of these old canals that they are still in use for modern irrigation.

The manufacture of Pueblo Indian pottery was and still is a major industry. The Indians did not know the potter's wheel and used the coil method of forming the pot, rolling clay between their hands until a "snake" or strip of clay was made. The pot was then built up by applying these strips around and around a base until the desired shape and size was attained. Many variations were employed in finishing off the piece of pottery. Sometimes the pot was scraped and smoothed or polished with a pebble before firing. At other times the spiral of clay was left intact, to form a pleasing pattern. Black pottery is still popular, and white, red, or buff-colored surfaces with designs painted in black are still made.

The Southwest contains three separate cultures: the Indian, the Spanish, and the English-speaking American. In many cases two or all of these differing ways of life are blended into a fourth and new culture. But in many parts of the Southwest the inhabitants hold to the ways of their ancestors, whether they were Indian, Spanish, or English-speaking European.

The early Spanish – Cabeza de Vaca, de Niza, Coronado, and others – impressed the externals of civilization on the Indians, although not without much bloodshed. After their subjugation by the conquerors, the Pueblo Indians abandoned those structures that were not easily defended and looked for more isolated and impregnable building sites. They moved to mesa tops where attackers would find it harder to reach them. Thus, after the Spanish conquest, many of the old Indian sites were left to fall into ruin and have never since been lived in.

Today you will find the great Hopi villages, among which are Walpi, Hano, and Oraibi. Countless people have visited the villages of Taos, Santa Clara, San Ildefonso, and Tesuque. Adobe brick is used in many of the structures, as well as stone and wood.

Weaving is still done, although mail-order houses and their wares seem to cut down the production of the old fabrics. In past centuries, Navajo weaving offered serious competition to the Hopi and the Zuñi product.

The Navajos, a pastoral people, do not live in community houses such as the Pueblo Indians build. Their winter house, called a hogan, is an earth-covered lodge made with large logs which form a support, while smaller logs and brush give a foundation for the covering of earth. A hole in the roof permits the smoke to escape.

The Spanish brought sheep and horses to the Southwest, and the Indians were quick to learn how to use horses for transportation and sheep for food and for wool. They raised sheep on a large scale, sheared them, and spun the wool into yarn for blankets and rugs. As time went on, they became very proficient at weaving, as they still are today.

They wash the wool in a solution of yucca root and hot water. It is then hand-carded and spun on a primitive spindle consisting of a stick with a wooden disk at the bottom to twirl the wool into yarn. Native vegetable dyes are made from sumac,

CLIFF DWELLINGS near Cottonwoods, Oak Creek Canyon, Arizona. These prehistoric people built their stone and mud homes in almost inaccessible places to give them protection against enemies. *American Airlines*

PUEBLO BONITO DOORWAY in one of the large communal houses at Pueblo Bonito, prehistoric Indian dwelling site at Chaco Canyon National Monument, New Mexico. These walls are about 800 years old. *New Mexico State Tourist Bureau*

piñon gum, alder bark, and various roots. Commercial dyes are also used.

The loom on which the Navajos weave is a simple frame with the warp placed vertically. Weaving is done from the bottom and the yarn is not placed in a shuttle but inserted between the threads of the warp with the weaver's fingers or with a small stick. A beater presses down the work as it goes along. Common designs include horizontal stripes, squares, diamonds, and triangles.

Navajos are also expert silversmiths and their work is famous all over the world. Ordinarily they use Mexican silver coins and set their jewelry with blue-green pieces of turquoise which they mine where they live.

Visitors to the Southwest still are thrilled when they encounter an old Indian gentleman, wrapped in a blanket, uncreased broad-brimmed hat set squarely on his head, the ends of his hair braided with red ribbons, and his pierced ears hung with pieces of turquoise. Many Indians who live on their reservations still hold to the old way of life even though their home may carry a television aerial on the roof. But visitors may pass off-reservation Indians on the streets of southwestern cities and may not even realize that the passing man dressed in Irish tweeds is of Indian blood.

Government schools and public schools have made a great change in Indian life. Boys are required to keep their hair cut short and to dress as their white classmates do. They play football, basketball, tinker with second-hand automobiles, listen to rock-and-roll, and may be found in the corner drugstore with their friends.

The Spanish-speaking Americans are descended from the conquistadores and the visitor to the Southwest will find a combination of Spanish-Indian-Anglo-American influences at work. In home architecture, for example, he will enter a Spanish-style house with red-tiled corrugated roof, a patio, Indian pottery and rugs, and a modern kitchen that might have come out of the pages of a homemaker's magazine.

Even in food preferences, there is a Spanish flavor. You can order tortillas, enchiladas, chili con carne and other dishes of Spanish-American origin from the same menu that carries pork and beans or ham and eggs. The influence is also found in the

INDIAN CRAFTSMANSHIP in silver and mosaic made by New Mexico silversmiths. *New Mexico State Tourist Bureau*

[OVERLEAF]

DEATH VALLEY, California. In the summer the temperatures in Death Valley may rise as high as 134°F in the shade. Its name is derived from the tragic experiences of emigrant trains that perished in the attempt to cross it. *Union Pacific Railroad Colorphoto*

NAVAJO BLANKETS are famous for their color and design and are made by the women of the tribe. A typical hogan or Navajo home is in the background.

language. Perhaps the only Spanish the Anglo-American knows is "*Como esta, amigo?*" or "*Adios,*" yet the flavor is there.

The early days are reflected in the clothing of the residents of the Southwest. The cowboy wore practical clothing for the job he had to do on the range. The visitor may think the costume is picturesque but to the cowman it is his work clothes: blue jeans, boots, and big hat.

The blue jeans are practical because they are first of all inexpensive, are usually copper-riveted at the points of strain, are slim in the leg, low at the waist, and are best suited for riding. Denim is tough and withstands the wear and tear of being tumbled in the dust or being dragged along by a balky steer when the only brake there may be is the seat of the pants.

The cowboy boots, with their high heels, are not particularly suited for walking. But the heels give the rider a better grip in the stirrup, the pointed toes make it easier to find the stirrup in a hurry, and the tops are loose-fitting so that the boots can be kicked off should a horse drag its rider with one foot in a stirrup. Forty dollars a pair is not expensive, and tooled and silver-mounted boots may cost a great deal more.

The cowboy's big-brimmed hat is also functional. It keeps the sun off him, sheds the rain, and may serve as a water-carrier if needed. Fine hats also may cost hundreds of dollars.

The rodeos that are held every year and the popularity of singing cowboys have had a definite influence on the cowboy's clothing. His work clothes are plain denim, with perhaps a gay shirt in his saddlebag. But he may also own some silk shirts, tooled leather boots, silver-mounted riding gear, and a hat that cost a hundred dollars or more — particularly if he has won an event or two at a rodeo competition. Even businessmen of the Southwest like to wear fancy cowboy clothing, and the average tourist returns home with at least a tooled leather belt or a brightly-colored neckerchief.

The cowboy and his language are part of our national culture and many expressions he uses have crept into our daily speech. We may say somebody was "roped in," or "hog-tied." The expression "pulling leather" is from the greenhorn's panicky tendency to grab the saddle horn instead of the reins when the going gets rough. And the sale of guitars inlaid with ivory and mother-of-pearl must have jumped considerably since the advent of television!

To sum up, the Southwest is, like the rest of the United States, made up of people and places and traditions. But they are so sharply different from the East or the Middle or Far West or the South that visitors to the Southwest find it one of the most interesting and beautiful regions in the nation.

Distance-empurpled mountains whose snowy caps seem only a mile away in the crystal air; skies as blue as cornflowers; deserts that are every color in the rainbow; formations in stone that are worn by the elements into every conceivable shape; cacti, sagebrush, creosote bush, tumbleweed, rattlesnakes and Gila monsters; peppery foods, cowboys, and Indians — all these are stereotypes of the Southwest, as tulips and wooden shoes and dikes and windmills are stereotypes of Holland. But in the Southwest, the "stereotypes" are true!

NAVAJO SILVERSMITH at work. His tools are crude but his jewelry is imaginative and beautiful. *New Mexico State Tourist Bureau*

PRICKLY PEAR. The Prickly Pear has characteristic big, flat stems which may number several hundred on one plant. Height: 1½ to 4 feet. *The Shostal Agency*

DOGWOOD BLOSSOM. The flowering dogwood's blossom has four bracts of creamy white, sometimes tipped with magenta or pink. Height: 10 to 80 feet.

The Trees, Flowers and Shrubs of the Southwest

BY PEGGY PICKERING LARSON

IN THE southeastern corner of Arizona a dirt road meanders through an adobe-shack ghost town, and then passes into a desert grassland. This is not lush grazing country — you seldom see cattle — for this land can barely support one cow on each sixty acres. Ranches are few. Only yuccas, an occasional stunted mesquite tree, and the view of distant mountains break the vastness of the scene. Traveling through this wide landscape you whiz past a most improbable sign, CAUTION — WATCH FOR LOGGING TRUCKS. If you are new to this area you wonder if the sign is a joke; if you have been in the Southwest any length of time, the caution comes as no great surprise. *Aficionados* of this corner of the United States know that much of it is an immense area of desert, surrounding mountain peaks that rise abruptly yet gracefully from the desert floor. If you continue to follow this same desert road, within 45 minutes you may find yourself in the land of the tall pines, home of deer, bears, flocks of wild turkeys, and the center of one of the many logging areas of the Southwest.

From deserts to mountaintops, from the Mexican border to more than a third of the way to the Canadian border, and from western Texas and Oklahoma to southern California stretches the area called the Southwest. The varied topography and climatic conditions of such a huge area combine to produce here a multitude of different types of vegetation, many of them strikingly different from those found in other parts of our country. This is the heart of the land of the cactus, and many people think of the Southwest only in terms of desert. Yet this is also the only section of the United States in which are found both arctic plants and those belonging to genera that are primarily tropical in occurrence.

Grasslands of the Great Plains sweep downward from Kansas, cross western Oklahoma, and in western Texas, southern New Mexico, and southern Arizona blend into desert country. The deserts

A FOREST OF SAGUARO CACTI, Saguaro National Monument, sixteen miles east of Tucson, Arizona. Height: 20 to 40 feet. *National Park Service*

march across most of the southern portion of the Southwest, swing up through southeastern California and billow out across Nevada and Utah. Much of northern New Mexico and southeastern Arizona are mountainous and support high mountain forms of plants. Near the center of Arizona is the Mogollon Rim, an almost vertical cliff running for many miles from east to west, and rearing some 1,000 feet above the desert below. This is the striking entrance to the plateau country of northern Arizona and northwestern New Mexico. Through these plateaus cut the Colorado River and its tributaries to form the Grand Canyon and lesser gorges. This plateau country ranges in elevation from 5,000 to 9,000 feet, and in certain portions sustains a high mountain flora. One of these plateaus in particular, the Kaibab, is the home of one of the largest virgin forests remaining in the United States. The word Kaibab is of Paiute Indian origin and means "mountain lying down," as indeed it is, since it supports mountain vegetation and is approximately 40 miles wide and 60 miles long. In other sections this is the eroded, beautiful, and immense country of the Painted Desert and the Navajo Indians. Here the land often nurtures little more plant life than sagebrush. These plateaus blend into the southern portion of the Great Basin or Sagebrush Desert of Utah and Nevada.

This, then, is the Southwest. It bears a plant life of several thousand species, and in order to discuss a very, very small fraction of the more interesting and representative of these, let's consider the flora of the Southwest in terms of life-zones.

If you were to take a trip from the Equator to the Arctic, and stayed at or near sea level, you would pass through belts of various types of vegetation. These belts with their characteristic types of flora were termed life-zones by Dr. C. Hart Merriam. Traveling up a mountain is similar to going northward from the Equator, and in going up you also pass through ascending life-zones, for traveling 1,000 feet up a mountain is roughly

LIKE ORGAN PIPES or a many-fingered hand, the cactus stands as a symbol of the Southwest. *National Park Service*

KAIBAB NATIONAL FOREST, Arizona. In the fall the aspens turn golden yellow on the road to the Grand Canyon. *Union Pacific Railroad Colorphoto*

equal to traveling 300 miles north at sea level.

All of the Merriam life-zones are present in the Southwest with the exception of one, the Tropical. The Grand Canyon area affords an amazing telescopic view of life-zones. The Canyon itself is a mile deep. If you were to take one of the trails and hike — or more likely you'd prefer to go muleback — from the bottom of the Canyon, you would start in the Lower Sonoran zone and pass through the Upper Sonoran zone. If you emerged from the Canyon on the South Rim you would find yourself in the pine forests of the Transition zone. Ascend the opposite side and you would arrive on the North Rim in the beautiful fir forests of the Canadian life-zone. The Hudsonian and Arctic-Alpine zones are not represented at the Canyon, but are present on the San Francisco Peaks to the south only fifty miles away. Usually the vegetation of all these zones gradually blends from one to another, and many plants are present in more than one zone. There are, however, certain plants which are dominant in each of the life-zones.

Cold winds sweep across the highest of these life-zones, the Arctic-Alpine. This zone is found to only a small extent in the Southwest, on the very tops of a few mountains, such as the San Francisco Peaks and White Mountains in Arizona, and the summits of the Sangre de Cristo Range and Jemez Mountains in northern New Mexico. The Arctic-Alpine zone starts roughly

YUCCA. The yucca plant looks something like a palm tree, even to the brown dead leaves hanging down below the living ones. The blossoms appear in the late spring.

at the 11,500-foot level of the mountains. There are no trees here; the soil is shallow, poorly decomposed, and often extremely rocky. These summits are snow-covered much of the year and the growing season is short — often only July and August.

Small, low-growing plants form the vegetation in this inhospitable world. They must be able to grow, flower, and mature seeds quickly in the short growing season. None are found in any great abundance and rarely is the ground completely covered by them. Many form mats in the crevices between rocks. Representatives of this type of plant life are the cushion pink (*Silene acaulis*), buttercups (*Ranunculus eschscholtzii*), and saxifrages (*Saxifraga flagellaris*). These three particular species, while completely isolated here on the southwestern peaks, are also found growing as far north as the Arctic regions of North America.

The coldest, wettest, and highest life-zone in which trees grow is the Hudsonian, directly below the Arctic-Alpine. In the Southwest this is a forest of generally large trees, occurring at an altitude of from approximately 9,500 feet to 11,500 feet. The dominant species represented here are trees such as Engelmann spruce, bristlecone pine, and corkbark fir.

The Canadian zone stretches below the 9,500-foot level to approximately 8,000 feet. The domi-

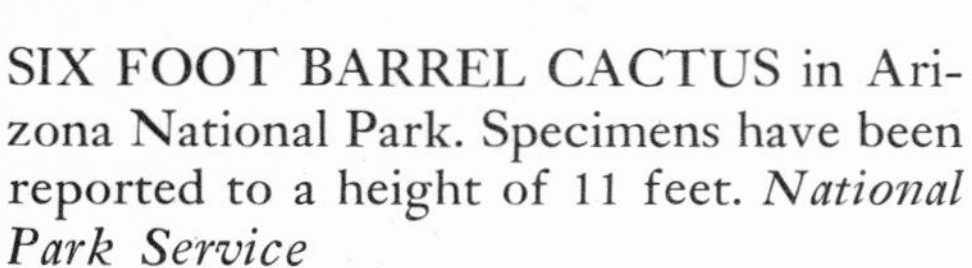

SIX FOOT BARREL CACTUS in Arizona National Park. Specimens have been reported to a height of 11 feet. *National Park Service*

THE JOSHUA TREE typifies the desert, with its characteristic gnarled branches and spiny leaves. Height: 20 feet. *National Park Service*

nant tree of this zone is the Douglas fir, although white fir, spruce, and limber pine are also present.

The ponderosa or yellow pine makes up the most economically important forests of the Southwest. This is the dominant plant of the Transition life-zone at roughly 6,500 feet to 8,000 feet. These pines compose the large virgin forest on the Kaibab Plateau.

The slim, straight, and stately quaking aspen is a tree that cuts across life-zone divisions in the Southwest and ranges from about 6,500 feet to 9,500 feet elevation. Dense groves of these trees form one of the most beautiful sights in the southwestern mountains. The white bark of the aspen contrasts with its dancing bright green leaves in summer, but as autumn quietly envelops the mountains, the leaves are transformed to a brilliant golden. These golden groves stand out vividly against their dark green background of pines and spruces, and can be seen ringing the mountains for miles away.

Here and there in the high mountains, the trees give way to charming mountain meadows. These meadows, filled with lush grass, fringed with aspen, and given a backdrop of spruce or pine, top off the whole with a multitude of flowers, such as violet penstemons, blue lupines, daisies, asters, and red paintbrush.

To describe the vegetation of the Upper Sonoran life-zone of the Southwest in a few para-

NEW MEXICO'S STATE FLOWER, the yucca, grows even in the gypsum sands of the White Sands in southern New Mexico. *New Mexico State Tourist Bureau*

graphs presents a task somewhat similar to quickly tracing the genealogy of a mongrel dog. For, in both, the components of the whole are varied and their distribution is sometimes hard to pinpoint exactly. The plants of this zone vary a great deal from one part of the Southwest to another; they usually occur directly above the lower deserts or desert grasslands at an approximate altitude of from 4,500 feet to 6,500 feet. The more important divisions of this flora are the piñon-juniper woodland, oak woodland, chaparral, and the varied grasslands.

In the plateau country of northeastern Arizona and northwestern New Mexico the summer days are often hot, but the winter is fairly long and some snow falls. This is an area where sagebrush appears in the lower elevations of this life-zone, and where juniper and piñon trees occur slightly higher.

Oak woodlands and chaparral (dense thickets of stiff or thorny shrubs or dwarf trees) form an important part of the Upper Sonoran life-zone, but the species of plants involved vary from one section of the Southwest to another. Bordering the western edges of the Mojave and Colorado deserts of California is a type of chaparral typical of that state, with manzanita, scrub oak, and chamise among the dominant plants. In the mountains of central Arizona is found another variety of chaparral dominated by shrub live oak, sumacs, cliffrose, and manzanitas. An oak woodland of Emory, gray, Mexican blue, and Arizona white oaks is found in southern New Mexico and in the southeastern and central parts of Arizona.

Great Plains grasslands or short-grass country is found widely distributed in northern Arizona, eastern, central, and northern New Mexico, in part of west Texas, and western Oklahoma. This short-grass prairie is quite different from the desert grassland which stretches from southwestern Texas across southern New Mexico and into southeastern Arizona.

Many of the southwestern plants of the higher life-zones are akin to, if not identical with, those

[ON PRECEDING PAGES]

PIÑON-JUNIPER FOREST. In this picture of a group in the Hall of North American Forests in the American Museum of Natural History, two forms of the piñon-juniper forest are shown. The large, relatively luxuriant forest in the foreground is growing on fine-textured soils derived from shale. The moisture and nutrient relations in these soils are very favorable for tree growth. The red soils in the canyon below are derived from a coarse sandstone formation and are low in nutrients. A sparse and stunted piñon-juniper woodland, frequently called a pygmy forest, has developed on them. The group shows a location in the Colorado National Monument near Grand Junction, Colorado, at an altitude of 5,500 feet. *American Museum of Natural History Photo*

CACTUS BLOSSOMS in Big Bend National Park, Texas.
Texas Highway Department

CHOLLA or long-jointed cactus, grows in the arid regions of the Southwest. Height: 3 to 8 feet. *New Mexico State Tourist Bureau*

[ON PRECEDING PAGES]

GIANT CACTUS FOREST. In the arid regions of the southwestern United States, as in arid regions over the world, many plants have become adapted to the meagre rainfall. Annual plants complete their life cycle in a few weeks during the rains, producing flowers and seeds, and die when conditions become unfavorable. Other plants, which live for several seasons, grow during the wet periods, then shed their leaves and remain dormant during the dry season. Still another method by which plants endure desert conditions is by storing a supply of water during the wet season for use when soil water is not available. The giant cactus, or saguaro, employs this method and can be seen to swell during wet periods and shrink during dry periods. The accordion-like structure of the cactus allows these variations without injury to the plant.

Photograph of group in the Hall of North American Forests, The American Museum of Natural History.

CRUCIFIXION THORNS grow in some of the arid parts of New Mexico. *New Mexico State Tourist Bureau*

PRICKLY PEAR CACTUS is only one of the many varieties that grow in the dry regions of the Southwest. Height: 1½ to 4 feet. *New Mexico State Tourist Bureau*

HEDGEHOG CACTUS. The hedgehog cactus is small and cylindrical and the flowers vary from red to purple. Height: 1 to 1½ feet. *New Mexico State Tourist Bureau Photo*

THE FLAT-LEAVED PRICKLY PEAR has large and spectacular yellow flowers which bloom in the spring. This one grows on Pajarito Plateau, west of Santa Fe, New Mexico. *New Mexico State Tourist Bureau.*

BARREL CACTUS. One of the most showy cacti in the desert community, the barrel cactus may grow from a few inches in height to 11 feet. *Southern Pacific Company*

GIANT DAGGERS in Big Bend National Park. These members of the yucca family are called Spanish Daggers because of the long sharp leaves. *Southern Pacific Company Photo*

CHOLLA CACTUS, Superstition Mountains, near Phoenix, Arizona. Height: 3 to 8 feet.

found in other parts of the United States, but the Southwest holds a near monopoly — and pridefully — on the truly desert areas of the Lower Sonoran zone of this country.

The southwestern deserts lie in the Basin and Range Province; this name signifies that the area is composed of mountain ranges separated by intermountain plains. The areas between the desert mountain ranges have either an undrained basin called a playa or dry lake, or have a drainage system of washes (stream beds, usually dry, but capable of carrying large amounts of water after a hard rainstorm). Water rushing down the desert mountains after a heavy rain forms alluvial fans of eroded material at the base of the mountains, depositing the finer textured soil at the outer edge of the fan and the coarser material on the higher levels of the slope.

Where playas are present in the desert the soil becomes alkaline, as minerals are left behind after the water evaporates. Salt-tolerant plants grow in or near these soils. Where dry washes are present trees and shrubs grow, taking advantage of the extra water found here. The intermountain plains are characterized throughout most of the southern deserts by seemingly endless stands of creosote bush. On the bajadas or alluvial fans and upon the mountainsides the coarser soil absorbs rainfall more readily, and supports more varied and luxuriant desert vegetation, such as Joshua trees, saguaros, mesquites, paloverde trees and many species of cacti — the plants present varying from one desert to another.

With many people an appreciation of the desert vegetation is an acquired feeling. At first sight, the desert plants are too bizarre and too grotesque to make newcomers feel comfortable. But as these people become more closely acquainted with the desert and develop an understanding of it and its hardy plants, they gain an admiration for the living things that successfully grow and propagate their kind here. Gradually the desert, with its highly strange forms of plants, takes on a kind of beauty born of this admiration.

Also, to many of the uninitiated, any desert is simply a desert — practically devoid of life, monotonous, and uninviting. The deserts of the Southwest prove this theory to be "all wet," even as the deserts themselves are not. In fact, the variety of plant life and desert conditions is so diverse that the Southwest has a number of different deserts, each with a vegetational character of its own. Often certain plants, such as the creosote bush, are common in several of the deserts, but the total aggregation of plants in each desert serves to set it apart from the others.

The piñon-juniper woodland of northern Arizona gradually grades into the landscape of the Great Basin Desert. This is an upland desert and is strikingly different from the rest of the deserts of the Southwest. This desert covers almost all of Utah and Nevada, and reaches into Wyoming, Idaho, Oregon, and eastern California.

In the Great Basin the green of the creosote

WIND-GNARLED JUNIPERS near Bluewater, western New Mexico. Height: 15 to 60 feet. *New Mexico State Tourist Bureau*

THERE ARE TWO beautiful desert plants in this picture — the agave in the background and the beavertail cactus in the foreground. Height: 10 to 15 feet. *Southern Pacific Company Photo*

bush, found throughout the southern deserts, is left behind, and the dominant color is the gray of sagebrush, *Artemisia tridentata* being the most common. This is not a true sage — the name has been given it due to its strong sage odor — but is a species of wormwood. Some other dominant plants of the Great Basin, all with improbable, flavorous names, are shadscale or sheep fat, hop sage, mule fat, and greasewood. Along the usually dry stream beds, cottonwoods and willows grow.

The Chihuahuan Desert is known as a predominantly shrubby desert. It is mainly Mexican in location, but tentacles of it reach out to probe into southern New Mexico and cover much of southwestern Texas. A type of agave known as lechuguilla, Spanish for "little lettuce," is prevalent here; sotol, or desert spoon, is so common that this is sometimes called a sotol desert.

Probably the most interesting of the southwestern deserts is the Sonoran, which reaches from south-central Arizona through southeastern California and also covers much of Baja California and northwestern Mexico. The Arizona portion of this area is sometimes called an arboreal desert, due to the large treelike plants growing there. In this desert is an outstanding array of desert vegetation over which the giant saguaro reigns supreme. The California section of the Sonoran Desert is drier and less rich vegetationally and is sometimes referred to as the Colorado Desert. Smoke trees, especially beautiful when covered with pale purple blossoms, are this desert's trademark. Palm trees,

AGAVE OR CENTURY PLANT. The life of the century plant is actually about fifteen years. At the end of this period, it grows a tall flower stalk, sometimes 20 feet high, then dies. *New Mexico State Tourist Bureau*

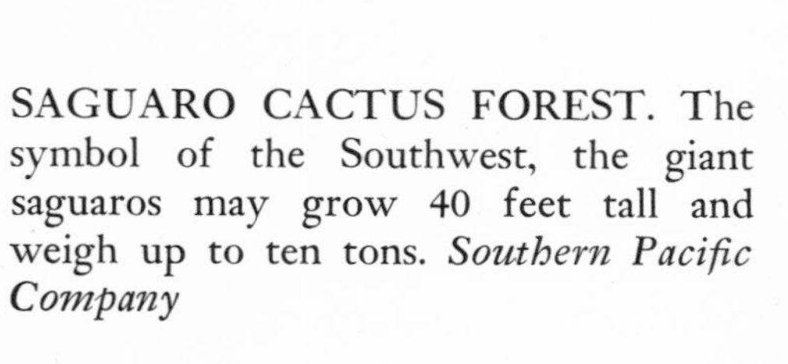

SAGUARO CACTUS FOREST. The symbol of the Southwest, the giant saguaros may grow 40 feet tall and weigh up to ten tons. *Southern Pacific Company*

MEADOWLAND near the little village of Las Trampas, high in the Sangre de Cristo Mountains, New Mexico. *New Mexico State Tourist Bureau*

in true desert fashion, also grow in oases here.

To the north of the Colorado Desert lies the Mojave Desert, which also reaches into western Arizona a short distance and spreads out over the tip of southern Nevada. This is a shrubby desert; it is primarily noted, however, for its curious, weird, and distinctive Joshua trees.

The principal vegetational differences in these deserts are due to varying conditions of rainfall, temperature, altitude, latitude, and soils. The driest deserts, receiving five inches or less of rain a year, lie in the trough of the Gulf of California. As the desert region radiates out from this area, rainfall gradually increases. The summer season is shorter in the northern deserts than in the southern, and conversely, the northern winters are more severe than the southern ones, having an effect on the range of certain plants.

Whatever climatic differences may exist between the deserts, there are basic similarities in all: relatively little rainfall, high mean yearly temperatures, high evaporation rates, and wide diurnal and yearly temperature extremes. All of the plants of these various deserts, when understood in terms of survival under these all-enveloping conditions, become extremely interesting. Here the terms "adaptation" and "survival of the fittest" take on a very real and obvious meaning.

The plants that have adapted themselves to stringent desert conditions over the years have managed this task in a number of near-fabulous maneuvers. Their methods can be divided roughly into three classes. Some are drought-escaping, others drought-evading, and the most hardy of all are drought-resisting.

Visitors flock to the deserts in the early spring to gaze at the riot of color produced by the drought-escaping plants. These are the annuals, which give the desert a fantastically gay beauty all the more striking when you realize that only days before the desert was clothed in subdued tones of gray, green, brown, and violet, and will return to those colors in a few more short days — for the desert annuals live only a matter of a few weeks. Their sole purpose in life is to flower and mature seeds quickly. These germs of future generations lie in a dormant state in the desert sand or soil until the proper conditions for their

DENSE FOREST along a winding mountain road in the Sangre de Cristo Mountains northeast of Santa Fe, New Mexico. *New Mexico State Tourist Bureau*

growth again prevail. They beat the heat by stepping up their life processes to produce seeds, which can withstand the more inhospitable desert seasons.

Many of these plants have close relatives growing in the mountains but certain modifications, in addition to the acceleration of growing, are apparent in the desert kin. Sometimes the leaf surface in the desert species is greatly reduced, or is covered with a waxy coating or with hairs to reduce the possible evaporation from the plant. Oftentimes the mountain forms grow to a larger size, especially in the stems and leaves.

There are two groups of these annuals. Some flower only in the early spring after the winter rains. Other species, although this group is generally smaller, grow only after summer rains. Desert annuals are all the more amazing when you realize that the seeds of the spring annuals do not sprout after the summer rains, and summer annuals do not grow after the winter rains. A variation in temperature requirements is the cause of this differentiation. Many of these annuals do not grow unless there has been more than the normal amount of rainfall for the year. If the moisture has not been sufficient, the seeds remain dormant during their scheduled time of growth, and, if the drought persists, the seeds continue to sleep in the sand for a number of years, until conditions are more suitable. Comes the year, though, of slightly heavier than usual rainfall and the annuals make up for lost time with startling displays of flowers.

The types of wild flowers of the southwestern deserts, and their mountain relatives, are almost as numerous as the colors of the ever-changing Grand Canyon and, like the Canyon, can never be adequately described but must be experienced to be appreciated.

Less showy than the desert annuals, but equipped with some amazing innovations for desert living, are the shrubs and herbs known as drought-evaders. It is in the leaves of most plants that their food is manufactured, yet the surfaces of leaves provide a large area for evaporation of moisture from the plant. Desert plants cannot afford to allow excessive evaporation — the penalty is death. They resolve the problem of needing leaves, yet sometimes finding them a handicap, in many different ways. Some have leaves that are

REDBUD OR JUDAS TREE. Against the blue sky, the clustered red flowers of the redbud appear at their best in early spring. Height: 10 to 30 feet. *New Mexico State Tourist Bureau*

YUCCA BLOOMS. The yucca depends on the Pronuba moth for its existence, and the moth is dependent on yucca seeds for food. *New Mexico State Tourist Bureau Photo*

covered by a thick, waxy or varnished outer layer, or with a coating of fine hairs to reduce evaporation. Sometimes the leaves are very small. In other cases the leaves may roll up, exposing less surface, or may turn as the day progresses, keeping only the narrow edge of the leaf toward the sun. Many plants, such as the ocotillo, have leaves only during favorable periods.

The weird ocotillo resembles a handful of thorny sticks set into the ground with each stick radiating out at a slight angle from the center. The limbs are usually bare, but put forth small leaves after a good rain; as soon as drying conditions prevail once more, the leaves wither and fall and the shrub rests, maintaining only the barest life processes until the next rain. In this way the ocotillo may grow several sets of leaves each year. Only when a plant is actively carrying on photosynthesis or food-making can it grow larger. Since the ocotillo has leaves for only a small fraction of the year, its growing time is short. The ocotillo may be 200 years old, but it is rarely more than 12 feet tall. Many other desert plants, like the ocotillo, spend a great deal of time resting and sacrifice large growth for a measure of security in their environment.

Cacti are probably the most admirable of all plants. True, they are not noted for their great beauty, except when they blossom, and they do not grow to any fantastic size or age, as do the redwoods. But still they have succeeded beautifully in what is essentially an inhospitable land. For the most part they take no pains to escape the drought or to evade it. They simply face the heat and dryness and resist it, using extreme modifications that set them apart from other plants. For these reasons we class them as drought-resistant. Also included in this division are agaves, yuccas, and certain trees.

The cacti have for all intents and purposes done away with leaves. The chlorophyll usually found in a plant's leaves is present in the trunk of a cactus, and the number of pores present is greatly reduced. Cacti are ribbed or nippled to allow for contraction or expansion, as they store water in their trunks for use in times of drought. They are solid and compact, for a bulky, columnar cactus exposes far less surface to the air than does a tree with its many slender branches and numer-

SAGUARO CACTUS. These giant cacti, the largest of the desert plants, make an interesting picture against the blue of San Carlos Lake in Arizona. Height: 20 to 40 feet. *Southern Pacific Photo*

ous leaves. A tree moves easily with each breath of air, increasing evaporation; the cactus cannot. Many of the cacti are coated with a waxy substance to reduce evaporation even further. They have, rather than a watery sap, a thickish juice which quickly coagulates in case of a wound on the plant. On some the areoles, from which the spines grow, are depressed below the surrounding surface to create a patch of still air to prevent water loss, and these depressions are often filled with a woolish substance for further protection.

The purpose of the spines on cacti and certain other plants is a matter of some conjecture. They do provide some shade for the plant. No doubt they break up air currents moving over the cactus, and to some extent they prevent animals from eating the plant, although this is far from true in the case of some small intrepid mammals who happily munch on cactus pads, seemingly oblivious to the thorns.

The agaves, commonly called century plants, and yuccas, often referred to as Spanish bayonets, also store water in their fleshy leaves. These long, narrow leaves are arranged in a rosette and are quite stiff, thus exposing less area and avoiding excessive movement which would afford increased evaporation.

Surprisingly, among the most successful desert plants, other than cacti, are trees which are members of the pea family. These are generally small (seldom over 25 feet tall), and of wide distribution, and include many of the major southwestern desert trees — the hardy mesquites, paloverdes, ironwood, cat's-claw, and smoke tree. Some of

GIANT DAGGER, Dagger Flat, Big Bend National Park, Texas. *Texas Highway Department*

these grow predominantly along washes, although the mesquites and paloverdes are often more widespread. All have extensive root systems to obtain moisture. When dry weather prevails they secrete waxlike substances over their leaves, if present, and branches. The paloverde's leaves are barely the size of a pinhead and are present for only short periods. Paloverde is Spanish for "green stick"; the green bark of this tree contains chlorophyll and takes over much of the job of photosynthesis. The smoke tree is a mass of thorns which carry on most of the food-making, and leaves are few.

The seeds of some of these plants, such as the ironwood and smoke trees, cannot germinate unless their outer coverings have been worn thin. This wearing action is accomplished as the seeds are rolled and knocked among rocks and gravel during times of tumultuous rains and flash floods. The trees are found growing in the most favorable of desert locations, along the edges of the washes, where the plants have taken root following this battering of their seeds.

Special types of desert plants grow in alkaline soil, such as that around dry lakes, where most plants cannot survive. Halophytes is the name given to these specially adapted plants, which include greasewood (not to be confused with creosote bush, which is often erroneously called greasewood) and several kinds of salt bushes.

There is a group of trees and shrubs in the desert which actually have not adapted to aridity but which grow only along washes or arroyos

JUNIPER TREES along State Highway 166, Davis Mountains, Texas. Height: to 60 feet. *Texas Highway Department*

where water is available, either on the surface or at some depths underground. The outstanding example of this type of plant is the cottonwood tree, whose bright green leaves clearly mark from afar the outlines of stream beds winding through a desert.

Plants on the desert's floor are usually spaced apart from each other, much as in a garden. Here water, or rather the lack of it, is the determining factor causing the spacing. Desert plants have extensive root systems to wring every possible drop of water from the soil. The cacti and some other plants, such as the creosote bush, have many roots near the surface to absorb water quickly before it runs across the face of the desert into the washes. Some, such as the ocotillo, may store water in their root crown. Others, such as the mesquite, have developed long tap roots that reach to water tables located at great depths.

Creosote bush even goes so far in its fight for survival as to exude a substance from the tips of its roots that kills other large plants that attempt to compete with it for its immediate water supply. This ethereal-appearing shrub has succeeded in being the most successful, widespread, and abundant plant of the lower southwestern deserts. Its leaves are small, evergreen, and are coated with resin to protect them from drying. This coating gives the plant a distinctive odor; the Mexicans call it "Hediondilla," meaning "Little Stinker." Actually many people consider its odor rather pleasant, especially after a rain. There are those who call it

A LONE YUCCA stands guard along the highway that crosses southern New Mexico west of Las Cruces. The arid regions of the Southwest support a surprising variety of plant life. *New Mexico State Tourist Bureau*

ARIZONA DESERT. After an infrequent rain, the desert flowers bloom in riotous profusion.

an ugly duckling, others who think it beautiful, but all agree that it is one of the most remarkable of the desert plants, for it will grow in arid areas where all else will fail.

If creosote bush is a symbol of the southwestern deserts, it must share this honor with a tree, which, while not large or ostentatious, is by turns a blessing and a blight. To the Indians and pioneers the mesquite was a source of firewood, fence posts, and building material for their homes; and it also provided shade in a sunny land and food for men and animals, where food was often scarce.

Mesquite is at times a shrub, sometimes a tree twenty or more feet high. The trunk is generally short, the limbs twisted and supporting a multitude of crooked twigs which sport bright yellow, narrow clusters of flowers after spring and summer rains. Species of this tree are spread throughout the lower southwestern deserts.

Indians valued the seed pods, eating them plain, cooking them, or fermenting them to brew an intoxicating drink. The seed pods are also valuable browse for animals. Why, then, is this tree a curse? It is not, and never will be in its desert home, but it has been spreading rapidly, reaching as far north as western Kansas and Oklahoma. Here it is crowding out the valuable grasses and usurping the water supply. The mesquite is a tenacious plant with a gigantic root system, which continues to send up new shoots when the original tree has been chopped down. The mesquite has moved out of the desert into the Great Plains following grazing of the grass-

SAGUARO CACTUS, Saguaro National Monument, Arizona. Damage to the cactus sometimes results in odd growth forms. Height: 20 to 40 feet. *National Park Service*

land. Difficult to control, it is, in its place, a useful thing of beauty, but in its move northward, a source of anxiety.

In the public's mind the two most popular symbols of the southwestern deserts are a pair of bizarre plants, neither of which is particularly widespread in distribution. These two are the Mojave's Joshua tree and the Sonoran Desert's saguaro cactus.

The Joshua tree is a grizzly, gnarled veteran of the desert, and looks like anything but what it is, a member of the lily family. It is known as a tree yucca. The plant has a definite trunk and limbs and the sharp, rigid leaves grow in bunches near the end of each limb. Clusters of whitish buds form at the ends of the branches. Joshua trees are probably among the oldest of desert plants, but their ages are not known for they do not form annual growth rings. Huge forests of them grow in the Mojave Desert.

The saguaro is the "grandfather" of all cacti, the movie symbol of the Wild West, the photographer's delight, Arizona's state flower, and, to a rather surprising extent, the Papago Indians' sustenance.

The saguaro is a columnar cactus, sometimes fifty feet tall and weighing ten tons. It is well armed with spines. Curious arms branch from the upper part of the plant, and generally stretch toward the sky. The plant is ribbed for water storage, and expands and contracts as its water supply is increased in wet periods, or gradually used during drought.

In the summer, when the temperature stands well over the 100°F. mark, Papago Indians set up camps in the vast saguaro forests. They harvest the red, pulpy fruit that has developed from the white flowers which earlier formed halos about the tips of the saguaro's trunk and arms. The fruit is knocked to the ground, gathered, eaten raw, dried, cooked to make a syrup or jelly, or allowed to ferment to make an alcoholic drink called "tiswin." The tiny black seeds, as many as 4,000 in each fruit, are ground into a sort of flour. The stiff inner ribs of the dead saguaros are used to knock the fruit to the ground, or are laid side by side and plastered with mud to form the roof for the Indians' home. Nature provides, even in the desert.

Where plant life cannot exist, other life, unaided, cannot either. It is plant life only that can combine, in the presence of chlorophyll, carbon dioxide, and water to produce sugar and free oxygen. The sugar is used by the plant as the building block for the basic foodstuffs of life, namely protein, carbohydrates, and fats. Animals, in turn, eat the plants to build their bodies.

Plants are, therefore, a necessity of life, but they are also the gifts of a Bountiful Creator, which add interest, wonder, happiness, and variety to our lives. There are probably few other places on earth where Nature has given so freely of her variety of plant life as in that land of the wide blue sky and handsome sweeping vistas — the Southwest.

FLOWERING YUCCA amid the gleaming white waste of sand in the great White Sands, a National Monument in southern New Mexico. *New Mexico State Tourist Bureau*

DIAMONDBACK RATTLESNAKE (*Crotalus atrox*). The western desert diamondback rattlesnake is the largest rattlesnake in the Southwest, some specimens being seven feet five inches in length and twenty-four pounds in weight. Length: 5 feet. *U.S. Fish & Wildlife Service*

DESERT TORTOISE (*Gopherus agassizii*). Travelers across deserts may often find desert tortoises plodding along the road. They feed on the fruits and stems of cacti. Length: 10 inches. *U.S. Fish & Wildlife Service*

The Reptiles of the Southwest

BY WILLIAM H. WOODIN *and* MERVIN W. LARSON

THE VERY WORD "reptile" carries an emotional impact surpassed by only a few other words, and the reptiles themselves are among the least generally understood and the most myth-ridden animals known to man. But the types and temperaments of the snakes, lizards, and turtles are about as varied as those of mankind and almost as interesting once you get to know the reptiles. There is no better place in the United States to learn about them than the Southwest, for, due to the diversity of southwestern environments, the types and numbers of reptiles present here outnumber all those in the rest of the United States combined.

Reptiles are cold-blooded animals with backbones, usually with external scales, possessing lungs, and not dependent on a moist environment for propagation. They are more advanced along the evolutionary ladder than are the amphibians — frogs, toads, and salamanders — but are one rung below the birds.

In the distant past, reptiles dominated the world in kinds, numbers, and size, on the land, in the water, and in the air. Now only a comparatively few remnants of this once-powerful group remain. The three major groups today include the lizards, snakes, and turtles.

Among these leftovers from the dinosaurs, the lizards most resemble their ancient ancestors, in form if not in size. In fact, some of the lizards will occasionally run only on their hind feet, using the tail for balance, as once the mighty *Tyrannosaurus rex* chased its prey. Today southwestern lizards range from two inches to nearly two feet in length. There are both poisonous and non-poisonous types, those with and those without legs,

HORNED TOAD (*Phrynosoma*). The horned toad is actually a lizard. It lives on the ground where its flattened body makes it almost invisible. Length: 4 inches. *U.S. Fish & Wildlife Service*

plant-eaters and meat-eaters, some that are born alive and others that hatch from white leathery eggs.

Lizards are extremely beneficial animals, for with only a few exceptions they are insect- and spider-eaters. Only one, the Gila monster, is known to eat young birds and mammals.

For the most part the lizards are active during the daylight hours although, contrary to popular belief, reptiles as a whole cannot stand as much external heat as mammals can. Mammals can control their body temperature by perspiring but the reptile, in most instances, has no way to cool off except to move to a cooler area. We see reptiles out in heat, but they stay out in an above-lethal temperature for only a few minutes. The optimum temperature (a temperature that the reptile seems to find the best for his activity) is very high in some kinds of lizards, and they flirt with death every day by being active at barely sub-lethal temperatures.

An interesting tale about lizards is found in their tails. Most lizards are able to lose one and grow another. This ability comes in handy as a defensive device, since a predator will often grab the twitching joint, which has become detached during a scuffle, and the lizard has a good chance of escaping, albeit tailless. Sometimes the tail may become only partly disjointed, but a new one grows at the break and a forked tail is the result. This same circumstance may even occur again, so that a third tail results.

Many individual types of lizards have their own

peculiar adaptations, which aid in their defense or in living in a particular environment. In discussing the following general types of southwestern lizards we will note some of the more outstanding of these adaptations.

By far the most universal and the best-known lizard occurring in all of the states of the Southwest is the swift. Its aliases include fence lizard, scaly lizard, blue-belly, and other names. Swifts are adaptable fellows found from high mountaintops to low desert floors, and although some species are ground-dwelling, others spend much of their time aboveground on rocks, trees, posts, and other such places. They are generally recognized by their rough scaly appearance. Their adult size varies with the species from three inches to a foot in length; and this group includes both egg-layers and live-bearers.

The name "blue-belly" is a popular one for the swift, because in most species the males have bright blue under parts and the females often have a slight tinge of blue. Lizards with this coloring are greatly feared in some parts of the country, although all are quite harmless. In fact, these are often the first reptile pets of children and do well in captivity, eating almost any small moving creature offered them.

Another of the very common lizards in all the southwestern states, and often the first lizard seen in the deserts, is the racerunner or whiptail. His long tail and the longitudinal light stripes down his back serve to identify him. Some kinds have checker marks almost obscuring the lines. One giant form reaches an extreme length of eighteen inches.

Lizards of this group characteristically flick the tongue in and out as a snake does, to aid smelling. Their food consists of many kinds of small crawling creatures but especially of termites, which are abundant in the desert.

One of the most grotesque of the lizards, and yet probably the most generally liked, is the horned lizard or horned toad. It is, of course, not a toad, but a true reptile. This is another of the egg-laying, live-bearing groups. Its food consists chiefly of ants, but also includes other small crawling animals such as beetles, worms, and spiders.

Camouflage rather than speed protects this lizard, which is nearly impossible to see when it is sitting still. The horns found on the heads of most species may also serve a defensive purpose, although not always in ways that benefit the individual lizard. Many a snake has met its death when, after swallowing a horned lizard, the horns have broken through its body wall, but by this time the lizard usually has been trapped as well.

Another of the horned lizard's mechanisms which might be called defensive is the ability to

WHIPTAIL LIZARD (*Cnemidophorus*). The whiptail is so-called because of its long, whiplike tail. Length of body: 3 inches, Length of tail: 6 inches. *U.S. Fish & Wildlife Service*

RED RACER (*Masticophis f. piceus*). The red racer is found in the Southwest and in Mexico. It seldom exceeds five feet in length. *U.S. Fish & Wildlife Service*

squirt blood from the eyes. Many lizards employ a so-called "swell mechanism" – the swelling of a blood sinus at the inner corner of each eye – to help force sand from their eyes. In the horned lizard this blood pocket ruptures and a stream of blood droplets may be ejected for several feet. This act does not harm the lizard, but may disconcert an enemy.

The horned lizard and also the fringe-footed sand lizard and the zebra-tailed lizard have developed a special type of nose which has a sink-trap arrangement that catches sand particles taken in while the lizard is underground.

Horned lizards make interesting pets and do moderately well in captivity; however, they are protected by law in the state of Arizona.

The following three groups of lizards are chiefly desert dwellers and are well adapted to their situation. They run very rapidly, often on their hind feet.

The first of these groups is the zebra-tailed or gridiron-tailed lizard, probably the fastest of all, identified by the black bars on the underside of the white tail, which is often held curled over its back and waved gently from side to side. With a sudden burst of speed, up to 20 miles an hour, the zebra-tail can travel over the desert floor and then seemingly disappear. Actually it stops so abruptly that the eyes of the spectator keep on following a "ghost" image and lose the real animal. Its diet consists of small insects and spiders.

The most uniquely adapted lizards found in the

BOYLE'S KING SNAKE. The king snake is a constrictor and eats a variety of small animals. It is immune to the venom of rattlesnakes, on which it sometimes feeds. Length: 4 feet. *U.S. Fish & Wildlife Service*

COLLARED LIZARD (*Crotaphytus collaris*). This colorful little collared lizard, characterized by its distinctive "collar" of black and white stripes, is common in the Southwest. Length: 5 inches. *U.S. Fish & Wildlife Service*

Southwest compose the second of these desert groups, the sand lizards. These are one of the few creatures which actually prefer the arid areas of wind-blown sand. As adaptations for this gritty home, their nostrils have a built-in sink trap, their color blends perfectly with the sand, their eyelids overlap, and their hind feet have fringes on the toes to aid in sand-swimming.

Sand-swimming means diving into the sand and moving a short distance through it to escape an enemy. A would-be collector finds it very disconcerting to chase a lizard across the sand, see it disappear over a dune, and then apparently vanish. The sand lizard makes a speciality of speeding over the top of a dune and diving into the loose sand on the lee side. However, by following the tracks and digging shallowly around their end, you can usually uncover the culprit. The sand lizard will eat any small morsel that comes its way and may even leap into the air to catch a fly. This lizard's range is very restricted: southern California and the southwestern corner of Arizona.

The third of these desert-dwelling groups includes the desert iguana, which may be fifteen

THE BANDED GECKO (*Coleonyx variegatus*) stalks its prey as a cat would a mouse. It has claws that retract instead of adhesive pads. Length: 5 inches. *U.S. Fish & Wildlife Service*

SKINK (*Eumeces skiltonianus*). The family of skinks make up nearly one-quarter of the existing lizards. Length: 2¾ inches. *U.S. Fish & Wildlife Service*

inches in length. This is the only lizard in the United States with a slight crest down the middle of its back. The body is cream-colored with brownish or reddish lines and spots. Only this species and the chuckwalla are considered vegetarians, although they do take some insect food. Driving through the desert, you often see these iguanas sitting under bushes — typically creosote bushes.

More than any other of our present-day lizards, the leopard lizard and the collared lizard remind one of the dinosaur *Tyrannosaurus rex*. These two lizards are closely related and are similar in size and habit. They have very large heads with extremely strong jaw muscles; they are also pugnacious and can deliver a bite hard enough to break the skin. Both are lizard-eaters, but occasionally eat snakes, insects, and spiders.

The leopard lizard is found throughout the Southwest, except in Oklahoma. It is tan with light crossbars and its name refers to the brown spots scattered over its body. This lizard likes lowlands and grassy or brushy areas, while the collared lizard, often called the mountain boomer, prefers rocky places. The collared lizard is found in all the southwestern states. Two black bars encircle its neck, and the males often are handsomely colored, with a green body, and yellow or orange around the neck. This lizard often runs on only its hind feet.

Indians of the Southwest at one time found chuckwallas tasty eating. These are the largest harmless lizards in the United States, sometimes reaching a length of twenty inches. They are a grizzled black and white or reddish and despite their pugnacious appearance are herbivorous. Chuckwallas live in rocky areas, for their protective adaptation is the ability to inflate themselves so that they cannot be pulled from a rocky crevice. The Indians, however, punctured the lizard's inflated body and carried him home for supper.

A not-too-common lizard found mostly in the southern states is the alligator lizard. It can be recognized by a fold of skin along its side. Its tail is usually quite long and its legs are small. This combination makes it look like a snake as it weaves its way through the grass. It is not typically a desert species, but prefers moist areas. Total length may reach eighteen inches.

Another secretive lizard found in all the southwestern states is the skink. It also prefers moist areas. Somewhat similar to the striped whiptail lizard in appearance, it has a shorter tail and is very shiny. Many kinds, however, are striped only when young, while the adults are brownish. Red is often found around the head or under the chin,

CHUCKWALLA (*Sauromalus obesus*) Kofa Game Range, Yuma, Arizona. The chuckwalla, if molested, inflates its lungs, making it impossible for an enemy to remove it from its rocky retreat. Length: 16 inches. *U.S. Fish & Wildlife Service*

as well as on the tails of some skinks; many, though, have blue tails. These lizards are usually found in grassy places and are seldom seen unless disturbed, when the movement of grass as they scurry away sometimes betrays them.

Only three of the southwestern lizards are nocturnal. One of these is, not surprisingly, the night lizard. Found in the extreme southwestern states, it is one of the least seen of all lizards. It is from about two and one-half to five inches long and conceals itself well under rocks and in plant debris. Its young are born alive.

The second nocturnal lizard, the gecko, is the only lizard in the United States known to make a noise – other than the Gila monster, which hisses. The gecko emits a high-pitched squeak when disturbed. Common to the desert areas, it can often be seen on the road at night. It may reach a total length of five inches and is often mistaken for a baby Gila monster. The gecko's eyes are extremely large and bulging. Its smooth skin appears almost transparent.

The most unique lizard and the only poisonous one in the Southwest is one with a name that suggests the very worst, the Gila monster. This largest lizard of the United States is found chiefly in Arizona, barely entering Nevada, New Mexico, and Utah. It reaches nearly two feet in length and can be recognized by its orange-and-black-beaded appearance. It lives chiefly on small rodents and eggs when it can find them. The appearance of the Gila monster is sluggish, but it can swing

COLLARED LIZARD (*Crotaphytus collaris*). The collared lizard is one of the most numerous and colorful of the desert species found in the Southwest. Length of body: 4 to 5 inches. Length of tail: 8 to 10 inches. *U.S. Fish & Wildlife Service*

GILA MONSTER (*Heloderma suspectum*). The Gila monster's venom is as poisonous as the venom of some rattlesnakes. Length: to 24 inches. *U.S. Fish & Wildlife Service*

its head and bite almost as quickly as a rattlesnake.

Of the hundreds of kinds of lizards in the world, only the Mexican beaded lizard and the Gila monster are poisonous. The bite of a Gila monster can be serious if the animal gets a good hold and is able to introduce a large amount of venom. Although it has no fangs for injecting poison, as a rattlesnake has, it does have poison glands, very powerful jaws, and many sharp teeth. By chewing, it can introduce venom into the victim's body. The effects are mainly to the nervous system, but also cause local swelling. As is true with most poisons, young children, persons in poor health, and the aged are the most seriously affected. Most bites are caused by human carelessness.

Because of commercial exploitation that threatened to make the Gila monster a rare animal, Arizona passed a law to protect it in 1952. It is the only animal with a poisonous bite that is so protected.

Snakes, composing the second large group of the reptile family, are the most recent development among the reptiles. They evolved from the lizards a paltry hundred million or so years ago. In the process they have lost eyelids and ear openings, and besides the obvious loss of legs have developed along the line certain other skeletal characteristics that make them more than just legless lizards. One interesting feature, for example, is the fact that the lower jawbone is not joined together at the front.

This is one reason why snakes are able to engulf such large meals.

The slender forked tongue is common to all snakes and is continually darting in and out when the snake is on the alert. It is often erroneously believed to be a "stinger." The tongue actually aids in smelling, a sense of great importance to the snake in detecting its prey, since all snakes are carnivorous. Of the other senses, eyesight is probably fairly good at short distances but hearing has been virtually lost. However, snakes can detect vibrations carried through the ground.

The Southwest is a snake collector's paradise; its snake population is extremely large and varied, with over 170 different kinds represented — well over half of the number occurring in the whole United States. They range in size from a foot to over eight feet and are found in all habitats below permanent snow: from sea level to 11,000 feet and from the driest deserts to lakes and rivers. In these pages we can but briefly discuss the more important species.

The gopher or bull snakes are perhaps the most predominant and conspicuous species to be found in our southwestern area. With the possible exception of the Mexican indigo snake which just enters southern Texas, these handsome yellow and tan splotched snakes are also the largest, with individuals occasionally measuring over eight feet in length. Average size, however, is under six feet.

Usually good-natured, gopher snakes when annoyed audibly voice their displeasure with loud

GOPHER OR BULLSNAKE (*Pituophis catenifer rutilus*) collected on Santa Rita Experimental Range, Arizona. The gopher snake is one of the most valuable allies of the farmer. Length: about 5 ft. *U.S. Fish & Wildlife Service*

hissing accompanied by rapid vibration of the tail. This latter is a common characteristic among many harmless snakes. Gopher snakes are very beneficial, as rodents form their chief diet; they are animated and highly efficient rat traps. This rodent habit more than makes up for the occasional egg or chick that they may steal from a farmer. Prey is killed by constriction, with the snake's strong coils suffocating the victim in short order, but not breaking bones as is often popularly believed.

Another group of constrictors, the king snakes, are usually gentle toward man but feared by other snakes, even the mighty rattlers. King snakes are immune to rattlesnake venom. Rattlers greatly dislike the odor of king snakes, and when a king snake approaches they assume a special defensive position with head held low and coils raised. In this position, quite different from their usual striking pose, they attempt to ward off the attacker. King snakes, however, do not prefer to eat rattlers, but like any small snakes; rodents and lizards are also high on their menu.

The common king snakes are usually black in color, ringed or speckled with varying amounts of yellow or white. Three or four feet is the average length. A smaller species, the milk snake, is ringed with red, black, and yellow or white bands. The name "milk snake" comes from the old myth that these snakes, often found around barns, actually milk cows. But they are quite incapable of any such feat, even if they did have a taste for milk, and their fondness for barns is due simply to a gastronomical interest in mice. Similar small, brightly colored species are the coral king snakes, or mountain king snakes, found chiefly in the southwestern mountains. These snakes are often mistaken for the poisonous coral snake, although

REGAL RINGNECK SNAKE (*Diadophis regalis*) collected in the Santa Rita Mountains, Arizona. Length: 12 to 18 inches. *U.S. Fish & Wildlife Service*

DIAMONDBACK RATTLESNAKE (*Crotalus atrox*) from the Kofa Game Range, near Yuma, Arizona. Length: 4½ to 7½ feet.

the bands are in different sequence (red next to black in the king snake, separated by yellow in the coral).

The racers and whipsnakes are the speed demons of the snake world. Although they cannot move as fast as a man can run, they give an impression of much greater speed, appearing to flow over the ground or through trees and bushes, where they are equally at home. The ones in the Southwest may reach a length of over six feet, but they are slim as compared to a gopher or king snake, and they come in many colors, some striped, some solid reddish, gray, or black. They are active at higher temperatures than other snakes, and, in fact, are practically the only desert species that is abroad strictly in the daytime; most other desert snakes do considerable prowling at night during the summer months.

Racers are not constrictors and have no means of subduing their prey other than just hanging on and starting to swallow, although sometimes they will use a coil to press the victim down. Their food usually consists of lizards and rodents, and some birds.

As might be expected from such an active and high-strung group, these snakes inevitably bite when handled, especially when they are first captured. Such a bite, of course, is quite harmless, although the needle-sharp teeth may cause considerable bleeding.

The patch-nosed snakes are small striped cousins of the racers, and are rather similar in habits ex-

SONORAN CORAL SNAKE (*Micruroides euryxanthus*). The coral snake is the only close relative of the cobra in the Western Hemisphere. The Sonoran coral snake is found in southeastern Arizona and western New Mexico, ranging down into Mexico. Length: 18 inches. *U.S. Fish & Wildlife Service*

cept that their activity is confined to the ground. Their name refers to an enlarged scale on the tip of the nose. Another relative is the handsome blue-black indigo snake, a Mexican variety which enters southern Texas. This is probably the largest snake in the Southwest, with a maximum length of eight and one-half feet.

Probably the most abundant of all snakes, especially in the vicinity of water, are the garter snakes. This large group, of which at least 17 varieties occur in the Southwest, is composed chiefly of snakes under three feet long with some form of longitudinal striping their predominant pattern. The tongue, an organ that aids in smelling and that is colored black in most snakes, is generally red with a black tip in the garter snakes. Another common, and objectionable, characteristic is the foul-smelling odor given off by musk glands at the base of the tail when the snake is annoyed. Garter snakes, like the racers, are not constrictors; they swallow alive the frogs and fish upon which they feed.

Occasionally broods of 60 or 70 garter snakes have been reported, and two dozen in a brood are not uncommon. This may help explain the abundance of garter snakes! Unlike most harmless snakes of the United States, garter snakes give birth to living young rather than laying eggs. The mother snake pays no attention to her young, which are entirely self-sufficient at birth. This is the general rule among reptiles, although a few snakes coil around their eggs, but again ignore the newly hatched babies. The myth concerning the babies crawling into the mother's mouth for protection may stem partly from the discovery of unborn young inside a mother snake, and from snakes having been observed swallowing other snakes for food. At any rate, the story has no basis in fact.

Although garter snakes are often called water snakes, the true water snakes are a related group that are the most abundant in the southeastern states. Several species, however, reach the eastern part of the area under discussion. As their name implies, they are even more aquatic in habits than the garter snakes, and instead of stripes, the predominant markings are brown blotches. They are also on the whole larger than garter snakes, reaching a length of four or even five feet. Like the garter snakes, they feed chiefly on fish and frogs and bear their young alive.

KING SNAKE (*Lampropeltis getulus californiae*) shown on the Desert Game Range, Las Vegas, Nevada, is a docile snake and seldom attempts to bite. Length: 4 feet. *U.S. Fish & Wildlife Service*

Another diverse and important group, of which half a dozen kinds enter our territory from their headquarters in the southern and eastern states, are the rat snakes. (More easterly varieties are known as chicken, fox, or pilot snakes, the latter name coming from the mistaken belief that they lead rattlesnakes away from danger.) The rat snakes are large constrictors on the order of the gopher snakes; southwestern ones reach a length of six feet. Their pattern is typically blotched, but is sometimes striped or even plain. Their food consists of rodents and some birds.

There are a multitude of smaller harmless species of snakes inhabiting the Southwest, but we will be able to give only passing mention to some of the more interesting of these. One such is the hognosed snake, the source of probably as much misinformation and needless fear as any snake — and that is saying a great deal. Commonly called the puff adder or spreading adder, it is believed not only to have a highly poisonous bite but a potent breath as well! The truth about this snake is stranger than the fiction. When annoyed, it puts on quite a show, flattening the forward part of its body and hissing and striking at a great rate. At this point it generally gets killed, or else the observer departs at a high rate of speed. Closer examination, however, would show that not only does the snake strike with *closed mouth*, but it is nearly impossible to make one of them bite! When the snake is provoked further it flops over on its back as if dead, its tongue dragging in the dirt. If placed right side up it will immediately revert to its former position.

Two beautiful slender snakes, the rough and smooth green snakes (the names refer to the type of scalation), enter our territory from the east. Virtually a solid green in color, these snakes are often found in bushes and trees where they blend almost perfectly with the foliage.

Another small greenish snake occurring throughout the Southwest is the ringneck snake, usually instantly recognizable by the red or orange ring around its neck, although this is lacking in one species. The underside of the ringneck is generally orange with black flecks becoming red at the tail. When annoyed, this snake frequently coils its tail in a tight thimble-sized spiral, exposing its bright underside coloring. The name "thimble snake" refers to this habit. Although similar in color, the ringneck snakes are very different from the green snakes in habits, since they stay on the ground and usually hide under rocks or logs.

Probably the two most easily likable snakes, for

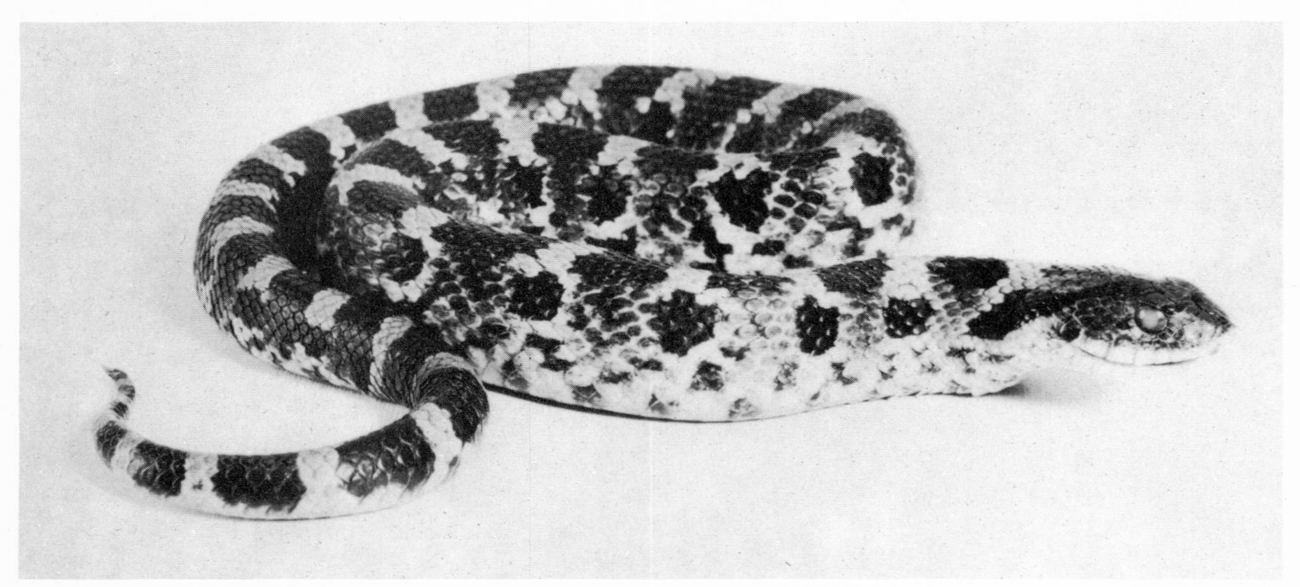

HOGNOSED SNAKE (*Heterodon nasicus*). The Western hognosed snake has a more pronounced snout than its Eastern cousin. It eats lizards as well as toads and small mammals. Length: 2 to 3 feet. *U.S. Fish & Wildlife Service*

HORNED RATTLESNAKE (*Crotalus cerastes*). More commonly called sidewinder, it moves over the ground in an S-shaped motion, traveling to the side. Length: 4 feet. *U.S. Fish & Wildlife Service*

those people who may be somewhat faint-hearted when it comes to this general subject, are the blind snakes and the rubber boas. These two groups represent entirely different families of snakes from any of those previously mentioned. The tiny worm or blind snakes are among the smallest snakes in the world. Usually under a foot long and scarcely bigger around than a matchstick, they live underground where they feed on ant eggs and larvae, and emerge occasionally at night. Their vestigial eyes are tiny black specks under transparent scales, and the color of the snake is a uniform pinkish rather like that of an earthworm.

The second of these groups includes the boas, represented in the United States by two small species, both under three feet long: the rosy boa and the rubber boa. The latter has such a blunt tail as to warrant the name "two-headed snake." These little boas are very slow-moving and are extraordinarily gentle toward man. They live chiefly on rodents, and, like their large relatives south of the border, are powerful constrictors. Boas give birth to living young.

In the desert areas, particularly, there live a large variety of secretive and often brightly colored snakes that spend the daytime underground and prowl at night. These include the long-nosed snakes, glossy snakes, leaf-nosed snakes, sand snakes, and others. Some, such as ground snakes and the tiny black-headed snakes, are sometimes commonly found under rocks. So are the spotted night snakes, which have a mildly venomous saliva of no danger

WESTERN DIAMONDBACK RATTLESNAKE (*Crotalus atrox*). This rattlesnake is one of the largest of our poisonous snakes. Specimens over seven feet long have been captured. Length: 5 feet. *U.S. Fish & Wildlife Service*

to man. The shovel-nosed snakes are the only harmless snakes with their colors arranged in the same sequence as the coral snake — red, yellow, and black. The red bands do not encircle the body and the head is not all black as in the coral snake.

Two rare but unrelated snakes which possess venom and grooved fangs in the rear of their mouth are the lyre snake and the vine snake. The nocturnal lyre snake has a wide head and a pattern of gray diamonds: characteristics which cause some people to think it is a rattlesnake without rattles. The vine snake is extraordinarily slender and may reach a length of five feet. It just enters southern Arizona. Neither of these snakes can be considered dangerous to man.

Now we come to the truly dangerous snakes, those having a pair of hollow fangs forward in the roof of the mouth through which venom is forced. Two great snake families are represented in the United States, with the majority of the poisonous snakes — the rattlesnakes, copperheads, and water moccasins — belonging to the pit viper group, so-called because of a pit located between eye and nostril. This organ enables a snake to detect the presence of warm objects at close range, such as, for instance, a nearby mouse on a dark night. Pit vipers are heavy-bodied snakes with thin necks and wide heads and they have long fangs which fold back against the roof of the mouth when not in use.

The only other poisonous snakes in this country

are the coral snakes, small members of the world-wide cobra family. They have short rigid fangs and small heads scarcely distinguishable from the neck. They are also brilliantly colored, with red, yellow (or whitish), and black bands completely encircling the body in that order. This color arrangement serves to distinguish them from all other snakes. The only wholly southwestern representative is the Arizona coral snake, which occurs in southern Arizona and southwest New Mexico. It is usually under twenty inches long. There have been few, if any, recorded bites from this species. A member of the larger southeastern species, the Texas coral snake, just enters our area in southern Texas. It occasionally reaches a length of three and one-half feet, and is a more dangerous snake. Coral snakes in general are rather rare burrowing creatures, nocturnal in habit and usually of gentle disposition.

Of the pit vipers, we are here chiefly concerned with the rattlesnakes. One variety of copperhead does occur in west Texas, and the water moccasin just reaches central Texas, but these are the extreme limits of their ranges. But some two dozen different kinds of rattlesnakes are found in the Southwest: three-fourths of all those found in the United States.

Largest and most dangerous of the rattlesnakes is the western diamond-back with an extreme length of over seven feet, although average size is under five feet. It is sometimes called "coon tail" because of the characteristic black-and-white-banded tail. Common throughout its extensive range which covers the southern part of our area, this species accounts for more bites and also more fatalities (a small percentage of the total number of bites) than any other rattlesnake.

Somewhat similar to the diamond-back, and often confused with it, is the Mojave, which reaches a length of only about four feet and is usually greener in appearance. The prairie rattlesnakes are a widespread and varied group of medium-sized rattlesnakes occurring practically throughout the whole Southwest with the exception of extreme desert areas. The Arizona black rattlesnake, a high-altitude form and the darkest of the rattlesnakes, is a somewhat larger member of this group. The only other large species of rattlesnake in the Southwest is the blacktail, a handsome snake vividly marked with greenish-yellow diamonds, and commoner in higher elevations than in lower.

The three smallest rattlesnakes, the ridge-nosed, the rock, and the twin-spotted, are all found in the higher mountains along the Mexican border. They are under two and one-half feet in length, usually

COPPERHEAD (*Agkistrodon contortrix*). Copperheads are usually found in wooded areas or among rocks. They are venomous but fatalities from a copperhead bite are relatively uncommon. Length: 30 to 50 inches. *U.S. Fish & Wildlife Service*

WATER MOCCASIN (*Agkistrodon piscivorus*). The water moccasin is found as far west as eastern Texas. Length: 40 to 58 inches. *U.S. Fish & Wildlife Service*

less than two feet. Two medium-sized rattlesnakes, especially noteworthy because of the high potency of their venom, are found in low desert mountains. These are the speckled and tiger rattlesnakes. Both may have a decidedly pink coloration and are rather similar in appearance.

The small sidewinder or horned rattlesnake is one of the most interesting species because of its unique system of locomotion, a continuous sideways looping of the body which gives excellent traction in sand. It is also distinctive in having a hornlike projection of the scale above each eye. The sidewinder is an inhabitant of the low, sandy desert of the extreme Southwest and does not occur east of south-central Arizona. Its light coloring blends well with the soil.

A final group, the pigmy rattlesnakes or massasaugas, are separated from all others by various features of scalation, including large plates on top of the head. Two species occur in the eastern part of our region, one extending as far as the southeastern corner of Arizona. They are not as small as the name implies, but may reach a length of over three feet. Their pattern is a series of blotches. Pigmy rattlesnakes are typical inhabitants of plains and valleys.

The rattle is the source of much misunderstanding. All rattlesnakes possess this organ, made up of a number of loosely interlocking segments which produce a buzzing sound when the tail is rapidly vibrated. A new rattle segment is added at each skin shedding, which normally takes place several times a year, and the end segments are continually breaking off. Complete strings of more than ten segments are rare, hence it is usually difficult even to estimate the age of the snake from the length of the rattle. It is also not true that a rattlesnake always rattles before striking. Sounding the rattle is a sign of irritation or nervousness and snakes differ in temperament just as people do; some use their rattle a great deal more than others do.

Rattlesnakes give birth to living young, averaging less than a dozen in each brood, although up to twice that number have been recorded. Each baby snake has a single rattle segment called the pre-button, replaced by the button at first shedding (usually within ten days). However, no noise can be produced until a second segment is added, an event which may not occur for six months.

Although small rattlesnakes may be chiefly lizard-eaters, the larger ones live principally on rodents and can thus be considered beneficial to man. They should no doubt be eliminated around residences or populated sections, but in remote areas one might well ponder the necessity of destroying them.

Turtles, the third group in the reptile family, are the antiques of the reptile world, having survived practically unchanged for two hundred million years. They are also individually the most long-lived of all reptiles — or any other animals. Some species probably live over a century and possibly as long as 150 years. They are also the most massive living reptiles. Some of the great sea turtles, of which several species occur off the California coast, may weigh well over one thousand

DESERT TORTOISE (*Gopherus agazzi*). The desert tortoise is a plant eater, living on herbs that grow on the desert during the short spring or summer rains. Length: 10 inches. *U.S. Fish & Wildlife Service*

pounds and perhaps close to a ton. All the turtles are characterized by the presence of an upper and lower shell, called the carapace and the plastron respectively, and by the absence of teeth. All are egg layers. Like snakes, they appear to be totally deaf, but their food habits are quite different from snakes', since some species are vegetarians.

As the majority of turtles are at least partially aquatic in habit, it is easy to see why much of the Southwest is not entirely to their liking. There are, in fact, less than twenty different kinds occurring in this whole region, and at least half of these reach only the extreme eastern part of our area, chiefly Texas. These include many members of the largest and most typical family, the fresh-water turtles. Their food includes both plant and animal material. These turtles usually have a streamlined shell, and toes at least partially webbed. One of the best known and colorful of this group is the western painted turtle with its red and yellow markings along the edge of the shell. Several of the closely related sliders or cooters are found in Texas; they include the red-eared and Big Bend turtles and the Missouri and Texas sliders. They are sometimes referred to as terrapins also. The Texas map turtle is another species of this group which just enters our area.

One of the best-known members of the fresh-water turtle family, but one with quite different habits from the others, is the box turtle. This is a rather small turtle, under six inches, with a high-domed shell. The name refers to the fact that this species is able to withdraw totally into its shell, the lower part hinging shut so completely that even a knife blade can hardly be inserted. Unlike the others in its family, the box turtle is a dry land animal, although individuals have been found swimming in rainpools. The southwestern species is known as the ornate box turtle, because of the yellow lines on its shell. It is found along the eastern part of this region, with a southern extension through Arizona.

The musk and mud turtles comprise another family of aquatic turtles, rather drab-colored and of small size. They may be identified by short fleshy appendages on the chin, called barbels. They also possess musk glands which secrete a foul-smelling odor. The common musk turtle just enters central Texas, while two species of mud turtles extend much farther west, one of them into southern California. This group of turtles is chiefly carnivorous.

The snappers are the largest, and probably the most famous, of all the turtles inhabiting the continental United States. They are also of considerable economic importance as food. Stories about

BOX TURTLES (*Terrapene ornata*). Two views of the ornate box turtle, showing the structure of their bodies. Length: 6 inches. *U.S. Fish & Wildlife Service*

them are legion and are often highly exaggerated, particularly in regard to the strength of their jaws. Contrary to popular belief they can inflict little damage on a broomstick, let alone bite it in two; but they are certainly capable of producing a painful wound in a human.

The huge alligator snapper, which may attain a weight of two hundred pounds, barely reaches central Texas, the extreme eastern limit of our southwestern area. The common snapping turtle, however, extends considerably farther west — from west Texas to central Colorado. It may reach a length of 13 inches and a weight of 60 or even 70 pounds. "Snapper" is an apt name for this species especially. Noted for its terrible disposition, it does not merely bite but actually strikes with the speed of a snake.

Besides their large size, the snappers are characterized by a small under-shell and a long tail. They are both carnivorous and herbivorous in habit.

The soft-shelled turtles, an aquatic group, are of a large size — up to fourteen inches — in the Southwest. They are very flat and thin, with soft, pliable shells and a neck that will stretch out extraordinarily far. They have developed to a considerable degree the ability to absorb oxygen from water through the lining of the throat; and as a result of this so-called pharyngeal respiration they are able to remain submerged for long periods, perhaps indefinitely. Two species of soft-shells inhabit the Southwest. One is confined to the eastern section and the other extends much farther west due to its introduction into the southern part of the Colorado River drainage.

The only turtles that can be truly said to be characteristic of the desert are the tortoises, and these are also the only strictly dry land forms other than the box turtle. They are the remnants of a great ancient group of land turtles, many gigantic in size, and mostly herbivorous. The shell is rather high-domed and the hind feet are typically shaped like those of an elephant. The desert tortoise occurs in the driest desert areas of the Southwest — southern Arizona and Nevada. It digs its own burrows or utilizes crevices to escape the extremes of heat and cold.

Besides obtaining moisture from the plant material which it eats, the desert tortoise manufactures some water itself through oxidation of food; and it is also capable of retaining urine for long periods of time — an ability which is helpful in reducing dehydration. A smaller species, Berlandier's tortoise, occurs in southern Texas. It is generally found in sandy soils and often in arid areas, although it is not quite as partial to actual desert conditions as the desert tortoise is.

SPINY LIZARD (*Sceloporus clarki*). Although this lizard seems to be of a suspicious nature, it took grasshoppers from the hand of its captor within an hour. Length of body: under 5 inches. Length of tail: under 5 inches. *E. P. Haddon, U.S. Fish & Wildlife Service*

BROWN PELICAN (*Pelecanus occidentalis*). The brown pelican, common along the coast of California, the Gulf States, Florida, and South America, catches fish by diving into the water and storing the catch in its capacious pouch. *L.W. Walker*

ELF OWL (*Micrathene whitneyi*). The little desert elf owl, no more than six inches long, usually makes its nest in a giant cactus. *L.W. Walker*

The Birds of the Southwest

BY LEWIS WAYNE WALKER

THE SOUTHWEST, encompassing tremendous mountains, flat deserts, and high grassy plains, has bird life of endless variety. From the California condors, giant remnants of the Pleistocene Age, to the many hummingbirds found west of the Rockies, there is an astounding diversity in size, shape, color, and behavior. Many of the geographical boundaries are extremely sharp, creating species especially adapted for a mode of life in a particular chosen habitat.

Some, such as the ducks and geese and most of the insectivorous birds, escape the winter by migrating southward in a directional pattern considered customary around the Northern Hemisphere. However, the rare mountain plover, member of a water-loving group known as shore birds, disregards family tradition and nests on dry grassy plains. After raising a family, it goes almost straight west over the Rockies and upon reaching the Pacific Coast becomes conventional and acts as a shore bird should.

Plovers, on their westward journey, pass over pines where evening grosbeaks rear their young. These black and yellow birds have their sights set toward the east, but this has not always been so. Their inclusion in the list of individualists dates back only a few decades, or to the widespread planting of box elder as an ornamental shrub.

As our civilization expanded below the Great Lakes, this bush moved along and was fostered. Finally there was an unbroken line of growth to the Atlantic Coast, creating a route of available food which did not exist before. Now the evening grosbeaks are no longer birds which seek warmth in lower valleys, but have become travelers along a seasonal path that is almost east and west.

Until a few years ago it was believed that the important habits of all western birds were known,

MOURNING DOVE (*Zenaidura macroura*) on nest. When the mourning dove takes flight, its wings make a characteristic whirring sound. Length: 10 inches.

even though the breeding and wintering areas of a few species were still to be found. Opinions were so set that it was thought that any bird relying entirely on a diet of flying insects had to migrate when such foods became non-existent.

And then a dormant poor-will, a species entirely dependent on flying insects, was detected in a rock niche on a California desert. This bird was watched for many months. Throughout the duration of cold spells which eliminated the insect supply it reduced body action and conserved strength by hibernation; it did not migrate. Since this initial discovery, other birds of the same species have been found in hibernation; and investigators working on the metabolism of hummingbirds state that the hummingbird also leans slightly toward hibernation by cutting down its bodily functions throughout periods of darkness.

Cowbirds and buffalos, burrowing owls and prairie dogs, are strange pairs which have been affiliated from time immemorial, and in each case the association is thought to have forced changes in the birds. In the days when buffalos roamed in uncounted herds they were in constant motion — moving, eating, depleting their food supply, and then moving on. Their shaggy hides were a haven for ticks and flies, and as the large beasts moved through the grasslands hidden insects were disturbed and forced to show themselves or be trampled. Although this was a banquet for birds that were free to go along with the buffalos, there were others of the birds left behind with the home duties of rearing fledglings. These were confronted with a scarcity of food for their young. As the buffalos sought new pastures they left the country denuded and the young cowbirds of that day starved in the nests. Thus, according to an accepted theory, the trait of parasitism commenced — a trait which forces our present-day cowbirds to fight their way into another bird's nest and lay an orphan egg that is hatched by the rightful nest-owner, which then rears the young one together with its own offspring.

The association of prairie dogs and burrowing owls is of common occurrence in the West, where the owls habitually usurp the burrows of rodents. However, in the retelling of the story, truth has been garnished with liberal imagination. Now most people believe that owls, dogs, and even rattlesnakes, all live in harmony in a single burrow. This is not true.

Prairie dogs are experts at digging and their

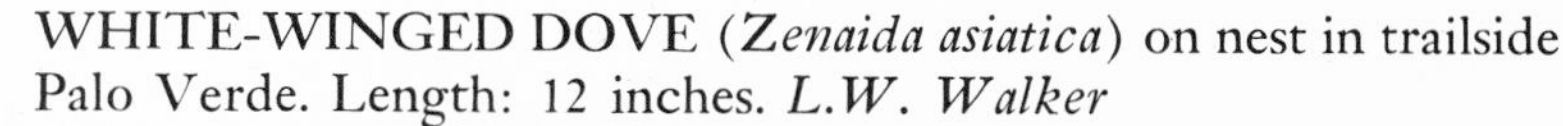

WHITE-WINGED DOVE (*Zenaida asiatica*) on nest in trailside Palo Verde. Length: 12 inches. *L.W. Walker*

colonies often cover acres of relatively barren grassland. Their burrows are the only haven of refuge for miles in any direction and are used by many animals. In the fall of the year prairie rattlesnakes congregate around some of these holes and retreat underground for winter hibernation when the weather becomes cold. Burrowing owls, which prefer prairie living due to the hordes of grasshoppers available as food, also take deserted burrows and scratch and enlarge a nesting chamber two or three feet below the surface. This selected hole is valiantly guarded. Snakes, prairie dogs, or any other animals that try to enter are usually driven away by the parent owls.

If logic had been used when this bird-mammal-reptile happy-family myth was concocted, the prowess of the animals concerned would have been taken into consideration. The owls, being carnivorous, would live on young prairie dogs, and the rattlesnakes in turn would feed on both rodent and bird and possibly even on the round white eggs of the latter.

A few years ago, while excavating a burrowing owl's nest on the outskirts of a prairie dog colony, I heard a rattling from the burrow ahead. It certainly sounded like a prairie rattlesnake. Days of observation which preceded the digging had proven beyond doubt that the hole was controlled by owls. I was convinced that they would not tolerate visitors but nevertheless the nerve-racking noise was there, becoming louder as each shovel of dirt was removed. Finally the nesting chamber was exposed. Crouched on the far side were five fledgling owls with open beaks, all mimicking a sound which could have given rise to the strange happy-family tale.

The southwestern states claim not only the largest and smallest land birds in condors and hummingbirds, but also the largest and smallest of North American owls.

The great gray owl is normally a resident of the Far North, but the Sierra Nevadas and the Rocky Mountains serve as long fingers by which the life-zones of Canada penetrate southward. Along the crests of these mighty ranges are trees, shrubs, and grasses which are completely out of place in southerly latitudes. Living among these plants are birds and mammals which thrive in these same surroundings whether they be located in the lowland plains of the Arctic or in the high altitudes farther south. Various chickadees, nuthatches, grouse, goshawks, and even ptarmigan, use ridges for a southern penetration, and in most cases there is an unbroken population that connects to the latitudes where these birds are truly normal.

The same Sierras which bring northern strangers into the realm of this book also create one of the greatest deserts in the world by absorbing western rainfall before it has a chance to drench the eastern slopes of the mountains. This has created a line of demarcation so apparent from an airplane that it seems like a surveyor's line — on one side pines, oaks, and other plants that must have rain in order to germinate and survive, on the other side creosote, greasewood and cacti which can live on either a minimum of water or can store moisture through drought seasons and replenish when the next rains fall.

With the abrupt change in growth there is also a similar abrupt change in bird life. In some instances this is so great that the effect seems like that of two separate worlds. The color and gaudy patterns which adorn the birds of the west side merge to drab shades which blend with rocks, barren soil, and glaring sand. This effect is constant to the east as Death Valley is crossed, and although disrupted by the waters of the Colorado River it is picked up again on the saguaro-strewn deserts of Arizona. It continues eastward until distance minimizes the influence of the coastal ranges and terminates the boundaries of the Sonoran life-zone.

Birds in this inhospitable land of cactus are specialists. Throughout the ages there has been a struggle for existence and only those best suited have survived. But this suitability is sometimes extremely disparate. Some have changed to become the largest and strongest members of their clan, while others such as the diminutive elf owls have shrunk to become the smallest examples of their family in the world.

HORNED OWL (*Bubo virginianus*). This downy young horned owl, near Yuma, Arizona, is already a fierce and vicious bird of prey. *U.S. Fish & Wildlife Service*

These sparrow-sized owls are almost exclusively dependent on the world's largest cactus, and wherever saguaros or cardons are found elf owls are resident nearby. However, their secretive natures and nocturnal habits make them extremely difficult to observe and they are better known by a wide variety of calls than by sight. Observations made at a nest on the grounds of Tucson's Desert Museum have shown them to live almost exclusively on insects and arachnids, and in the latter class they seem to prefer the deadly scorpions. These are brought to the fledgling owls with the stinger either mangled or completely removed.

The importance of the saguaro cactus to desert bird life cannot be overrated. Its branching arms are used by hawks, ravens, and large owls as nesting sites, and in many areas these cacti are the only sites available for miles around. The blossoms draw insects and become bird cafeterias all during the blooming season, and with the ripening of the fruits the plants extend their usefulness by supplying food until late summer. But from a bird's-eye view the plants' air-conditioned cavities are probably most important in this arid region where temperatures not only drop to freezing but also rise to over 115°F.

During the interim between winter and summer rains the Gila woodpecker, commonest member of the family to be found on the desert, starts house-hunting and pecks holes into the interior of the sturdy saguaro trunks. Aside from a circle of longitudinal ribs the plant has a wet watermelon consistency, slimy when bruised or cut; but during dry seasons a liquid is exuded which hardens upon contact with air. Hence, soon after the woodpecker's home is completed its walls solidify and it becomes encased with a moisture-proof woody substance. In years to follow, these holes are deserted

YOUNG OF BURROWING OWL (*Speotyto cunicularia*).
Length: 9 inches at full growth.

by the original builders and are subsequently occupied by flycatchers, martins, sparrow hawks, and other species which prefer to nest in snug little cavities.

Experiments conducted at Tucson's Desert Museum have demonstrated the ability of saguaro cactus to stabilize temperatures. In hot weather some of the excessive moisture of the plant is lost through evaporation and this, like a commercial evaporative cooler, creates a drop in temperature which cools these bird apartments. During short cold spells the waxy surface and the water-filled cells insulate and retain the heat within, bridging periods of inclemency.

White-winged doves and saguaros have a definite affinity and in the spring of the year the arrival of the birds from Mexico may be accurately timed by the first appearance of flower buds on the crowns of the plant. The doves then remain in the area and construct shabby nests in low desert growth or even on the arms of the saguaros. They feed on the white waxy flowers and then on the red fruits which follow. By late summer the last of the seeds fall to the ground and within a few days of their disappearance the doves form into flocks and migrate southward.

Many bird residents of the desert seem capable of surviving without free water, by obtaining mois-

CALIFORNIA CONDOR (*Gymnogyps*) is fully as large as its South American cousin. Today there are only a few California condors in existence.

ture from the foods which they eat. However, all four species of doves — white-winged, mourning, Inca, and Mexican ground doves — must head for waterholes at least twice a day. Some of these drinking spots are often miles from the doves' chosen homes, but as the thirsty birds leave their nesting areas their route will be straight and unwavering. This straight flight to water is a dove characteristic known and used by Indians to locate water since time immemorial. A few years ago a simple triangulation based on doves in flight directed the author to a rumored but unlocated waterhole in an extremely arid section of the desert.

Cuckoos the world over are usually about the size of pigeons or smaller, live in bushes and trees, and are rarely seen on the ground. However, the desert has a non-conformist in the roadrunner, a strange pheasant-sized representative of the family. Most cuckoos migrate and head southward when cold weather approaches, but roadrunners are sedentary permanent residents wherever found. To migrate, the powers of flight must be good. It is, in most cuckoos; but this member of the family earned its name by preferring terrestrial travel, and its flights rarely exceed one hundred feet, and then only when it is hard-pressed.

Another trait of the many cuckoos found around the world makes them cowbird-like parasites on

MOCKINGBIRD (*Mimus polyglottos*). The scientific name of this Texas mockingbird — the state bird of Texas — means "many tongues." It mimics almost every other bird in the neighborhood and has a marvelous repertoire of songs of its own. Length: 9 to 11 inches.

other birds which are forced to hatch their eggs and raise their young. But here again the roadrunners do not conform, for they are extremely good parents who construct bulky nests, usually in cholla cactus, and who raise their young to maturity with a true maternal instinct.

Roadrunners are practically omnivorous, dieting on a variety of food which includes insects, fruits, reptiles, and small warm-blooded animals. For about three months in the spring of the year, eggs and fledgling birds, including the young of quail, are high on their menu. During the remaining three-quarters of the year, however, roadrunners feed on scorpions, grasshoppers, lizards, snakes, and, most important, the young of various rodents. Poultry-raisers, game-breeders and biological research men all recognize rats and mice as the worst enemies of ground-nesting birds, and these experts claim that over 90 per cent of the nests in some areas are destroyed by these rodents.

Compared with their nine months of beneficial feeding, the roadrunners' three months of depredation tend to shrink in importance. The consensus of those best qualified to pass judgment is that the beneficial qualities of roadrunners amply negate the detrimental. The birds may be considered enemies of the individual quail, but a help to the species as a whole.

Fantastic creatures (and roadrunners fit this category) are usually the subjects for fantastic stories. One of the most widespread yarns is the truly mythical notion of how roadrunners kill rattlesnakes. It has been the subject of movies and folk lore, and has even been repeated in supposedly serious books as true natural history.

According to the tale a small sleeping rattlesnake discovered by a roadrunner is stealthily approached by the bird which carries a bit of cholla cactus in its bill. This is laid a foot or so from the reptile, and more cactus is added until the snake is completely encircled and held prisoner in a spiny corral. Starvation brings eventual death and then the patient roadrunner dines. The cactus and rapid starvation are obvious fallacies in this story. All reptiles can climb over cactus with perfect immunity, and most of them can go for weeks and months without food of any kind.

Roadrunners do kill rattlesnakes, however, but they do it by nimble movements and, on the desert, are usually assisted by the weather. When they encounter a medium-sized rattlesnake they spread their wings and tail into tremendous fans and also raise the other feathers on the body. This arrangement presents a large target for the snake's venomous fangs, but the roadrunner's body is small — a tiny bull's-eye that is completely hidden. The fans are used as a bullfighter uses a cape, and at each strike the reptile sinks its fangs harmlessly into the feathers. Reptiles tire rapidly. Each recoil of the snake becomes slower and then the bird steps in, administering pecks to the head of the reptile. During this entire battle the rattlesnake has been kept on guard, usually in the glare of a morning sun which is becoming stronger with each passing moment. Even if the repeated pecks of the roadrunner fail to render the reptile harmless the sun is lethal, as a snake's thermal tolerance is narrow. Forty degrees will slow it down to a wiggle, while a temperature of about 100°F. will kill it in ten or fifteen minutes.

There are several wrens found on the deserts of the Southwest. Most are small, good singers, industrious, and therefore typical of the family. However, one that the desert developed is exceptional — a veritable giant among wrens and the state bird of Arizona.

Throughout the areas in Arizona, California, and New Mexico where this cactus wren is resident, temperatures often climb well above the 100°F. mark. Most creatures then seek shade and

HUMMINGBIRD ON NEST [*cannot be identified without color*]. Hummingbirds live only in the Americas and are the only birds capable of true backward flight. Length: 3 to 4 inches.

try to conserve moisture by inaction, but this is not true of Arizona's state bird. Even on the hottest days it remains industrious, flipping over pebbles in search of insects, prying into the affairs of other creatures, or perhaps even carrying material for the building of decoy nests which litter the cactus wherever these wrens are found. Its range almost coincides with the range of cholla cactus.

The homes of the cactus wren are complicated, usually constructed of grasses which are woven to form a domed roof, with a narrow tunnel entrance which is six or eight inches long. Most wrens are prodigious nest-builders and it is not unusual to have house wrens display this family trait by filling a bushel basket to construct a tiny receptacle for the eggs in its center. However, to the cactus wren goes the honor of building the most nests. Some pairs will have homes in every cholla over an area of fifty or sixty feet. Only one of these is used for the raising of a family, and one might be used by the male for a nightly roost. The rest, in theory at least, are decoys to lure enemies away from the

BARN OWL (*Tyto alba*). The barn owl is a great destroyer of rats and mice. This specimen was photographed at Tishomingo National Wildlife Refuge, Oklahoma. Length: 15 to 21 inches. *U.S. Fish & Wildlife Service*

one which actually contains the eggs or young.

The industrious nature of cactus wrens is combined with an extreme curiosity and there is little that goes on in daylight hours that is missed by these birds. If a fox, a bobcat, or a Gila monster ventures abroad it will be followed by a group of these birds, each uttering a throaty churr as the enemy progresses through the home territories of various wren families. This calling reaches its peak when rattlesnakes are discovered. Herpetologists around Tucson, Arizona, investigate such calls whenever they are heard, in a new system of snake-hunting which is proving very productive.

"Pine-covered islands on a sea of sand" pretty well describes some of the mountaintops in southern Arizona and New Mexico. These peaks bring into our realm some of the strange rare birds from south of the border, such as trogons, becards, parrots, fool's quail, and several species of interesting hawks. Their presence in turn has lured most of the great names in ornithology to the region.

Wild parrots occurring in the United States have

ELF OWL (*Micrathene whitneyi*). Some owls are no bigger than a sparrow. The elf owl is only six inches long and is shown here at its cactus nest with a scorpion in its beak.

CANADA GOOSE (*Branta canadensis*). On its migratory flight, the Canada goose often stops off for refreshment and rest at the Desert Game Range near Las Vegas, Nevada. *E. P. Haddon*

always been rarities and when the Carolina parakeet became extinct, parrots, to all extents and purposes, were gone from our country. However, some of the Arizona mountain peaks form the extreme northern fringe in the range of the thick-billed parrot of Mexico and about once in each score of years they cross the Mexican border in large flocks. These green parrots, which are almost of macaw size, normally live along the crest of Mexico's Sierra Madre range where piñon nuts are rumored to be their main food. But every few decades the nut crop of the pines is insufficient and the birds forsake their normal habitat and travel northward from mountaintop to mountaintop. Only the most venturesome enter the region of the Southwest.

Beneath the pines and on down into the lower oak belt which encircles the peaks, the ground is covered with a natural litter. This is the home of the Mearns's quail, another Mexican bird whose northern range limit occurs on the United States side of the international border. These rare creatures are secretive or brazen, depending upon their mood. At times I have walked through these forests for hours, encountering thousands of freshly dug depressions made by Mearns's quail as they scratched for tiny bulbs, but not a single individual have I seen. A day or so later the same territory was traveled once more and in place of a scarcity

PINTAIL DUCK (*Anas acuta*). The pintail, so-called because of its sharply pointed tail, winters in the Southwest. Length: 26 to 30 inches. *U.S. Fish & Wildlife Service*

of birds there was abundance. Every few hundred feet the ground literally exploded as small coveys of quail rocketed into the air from places of concealment.

Woodcock, ptarmigan, grouse, and some other birds of the world are frequently mentioned as faultless examples of protective coloration. But most of these publicized examples will flush if an enemy approaches to within springing distance; in short, they haven't the courage to rely completely on not being seen. The Mearns's quail, however, have the courage of their convictions and rarely leave the ground until the leaves or grasses upon which they are crouching are actually disturbed by a footfall. Even when the birds are seen to land and crouch in a flattened position and the onlooker mentally marks the spot, they blend to the point of invisibility.

Incongruous stragglers from the south, buffeted northward by tropical hurricanes, have no doubt been seasonal casualties on the inhospitable desert for as long as birds and desert have existed. In recent years, however, dams have been placed on rivers that were normally dry throughout the major part of each season. These spots where water has become permanent beckon from afar and lure birds which formerly would have perished on the desert unrecorded. Thus the arid sections of southern

YOUNG WHITE PELICANS (*Pelecanus erythrorhynchus*).
The white pelican can soar aloft for hours.

California, Arizona, and even New Mexico, are seeing strange visitors that are strictly pelagic, such as boobies, brown pelicans, man-of-war birds, and shearwaters. In general, these strangers are seen briefly and then disappear. Some may make it back to their ocean habitat but most of them probably succumb, unable to cope with the unfamiliar environment.

But here again there are exceptions, especially around that body of water called the Salton Sea which was formed by an engineering blunder early in the twentieth century. Before this below-sea-level depression was inundated it was a sandy waste inhabited by lizards, sidewinders, roadrunners and cactus wrens; and the ducks, geese and cranes migrating along the San Joaquin Valley flyway passed high above it on their way to or from the lush delta of the Colorado. During the formation of the inland sea all the waters of the Colorado were diverted and the delta became a maze of cattails and willows which clogged the channels and ended this waterway's use as a navigable stream. It also lessened its importance as a home for many birds.

White pelicans, glossy ibis, stilts and avocets moved into the new sea and established breeding colonies, and until one quarter of the century had passed they practically ruled this body of water.

CALIFORNIA BROWN PELICAN (*Pelecanus occidentalis*) is common on the coast of Florida, the Gulf States, California, and South America. Length: to 50 inches.

SAGE GROUSE (*Centrocercus urophasianus*). Charles Sheldon Antelope Refuge, Nevada. Length: 15 to 19 inches. *U.S. Fish & Wildlife Service*

WHITE PELICANS (*Pelecanus erythrorhynchus*) and young. White pelicans live in the interior of the United States, nesting on islands in desert lakes such as the Great Salt Lake in Utah. Length: to 48 inches.

Then came some strangers in the form of gull-billed terns, birds normally at home along the Gulf Coast of Texas and eastward. Unseen and unpublicized, they surreptitiously established a colony and, before discovery, had multiplied to several score of birds. From the east coast came more strangers when two pair of laughing gulls set up housekeeping, but their reign was a short one. Three of the four ended in museum cabinets before any young could be raised.

Caspian terns were the next to drop in and look over the territory. They liked it, stayed to breed, and have maintained a sizable population. Now, fifty years after the Salton Sea's formation, it is one of the best birding spots in the entire Southwest, strangely combining the possibility of simultaneous observations on water birds, desert birds, and migratory species.

About a half mile from shore on the south end of the sea, small temporary islands are formed by a quirk of storm currents during winter months. These bits of land last until August winds roil the waters and erode the islands out of existence, but during their short life they are busy rookeries for some of the most spectacular birds to be found in the West.

When the Salton Sea is approached from the south, if occasional glances are directed skyward,

OSPREYS AT NEST (*Pandion haliaëtus*). The osprey or fish hawk has long, sharp claws for catching its slippery prey. Length: 21 to 24 inches.

COOPER'S HAWK (*Accipiter cooperi*). Shown at the Tishomingo Refuge, Oklahoma, this Cooper's hawk is sometimes guilty of seizing half-grown chickens for its dinner. Length: 14 to 18 inches. *U.S. Fish & Wildlife Service*

an observer will usually be rewarded by seeing a long follow-the-leader line of white pelicans. Sometimes these birds will be soaring at an elevation so high that only the silvery glint of sunlight on their feathers discloses their position. Aviators frequenting the area often encounter them at an elevation of about 6,000 feet. This elevation is approximately the height of the passes across the cool mountains to the west. As the watcher swelters at about 110°F. it is well to remember that the birds are soaring in a temperature of about 70°F.

These periodic flights to cool altitudes seem to be a form of recreation. Soon after the below-sea-level heat is left behind, the pelicans align one behind the other and stretch single file for hundreds of feet. When observing their progress, I have never been able to decide whether the leader was a sagacious old veteran, wise to the ways of thermals, or whether such mastery of air currents was instinctive to all. As they are watched it seems that the leader heads for the rising currents. Where he flaps, each of the following birds flaps also. Where he glides, they glide also upon reaching the selfsame spot.

All during the ascent each maneuver seems rehearsed and even during the time when the birds become glinting specks, orderly lines are apparent.

YOUNG BLACK-NECKED STILTS (*Himantopus mexicanus*).

THE ROAD RUNNER (*Geococcyx*) is a cuckoo that successfully kills rattlesnakes and can run at great speed. *American Museum of Natural History*

STILT (*Himantopus mexicanus*) at nest. The stilt is so named because it has very long legs, very useful for wading in shallow water.

DUCK HAWK (*Falco peregrinus*) with young. The duck hawk is so-called because it sometimes preys on flocks of ducks. It builds its nest preferably on cliffs or other high, inaccessible places.

RAVEN (*Corvus corax*), photographed at Spur, Texas. The raven is among the most adaptable of birds and ranges in isolated places from desert heat to arctic cold. Length: 24 inches. *U.S. Fish & Wildlife Service*

POORWILL (*Phalaenoptilus nuttalli*), playing "broken wing" to lure the photographer away from the nest. Length: 7½ inches.

WHOOPING CRANE (*Grus americana*) is the tallest bird in North America. It is on the verge of extinction, less than three dozen specimens being known. Length: to 44 inches. *U.S. Fish & Wildlife Service*

During the descent this order changes. Ranks break and each individual bird plummets to the sea below. Some close their wings and when they are opened several hundred feet above the nesting islands, their feathers vibrate and release a sound that can be heard for a quarter of a mile.

By early April the mud islands are dotted with shallow depressions containing the eggs of white pelicans. When they are first laid, the weather is still comparatively cool and the birds sit on the eggs to keep them warm. But with each succeeding day the sun climbs higher and ground temperatures soar to extremes which will cook any unprotected egg. Then the pelicans strive to lower the temperature by making numerous trips to the shallows around the islands, where they thoroughly dunk their breast feathers in the water. Dripping wet, they waddle back to their eggs and crouch above them with the damp feather tips barely touching the shells, so creating evaporative coolers which are seemingly very effective.

Newly hatched young are a vivid salmon color,

THE SNOWY EGRET (*Leucophoyx thula*) was reduced to the brink of extinction by plumage hunters but is now protected and is increasing in number. Length: 24 inches.

CACTUS WREN (*Heleodytes brunneicapillus*). The cactus wren makes its home in a cactus or mesquite bush, building it of sticks lined with grass. Length: 5 inches.

THE ROAD RUNNER (*Geococcyx*) is a most unusual bird. It is the state bird of New Mexico. It can run rapidly and is a great snake and lizard killer. Length: 24 inches. *New Mexico State Tourist Bureau*

CORMORANTS sitting on their cliff nest.

completely bare and with an overall waxy skin texture. Within a week after the birds emerge from the eggs a faint trace of down commences to cover the salmon-colored skin. This down grows rapidly and in three weeks the fledglings gather into small bands and waddle about the colony seeking shade under anything that will cast a shadow. If disturbed at this age, they usually regurgitate any food fed to them by their parents. Examination of this discloses such fish as carp, humpback suckers, mullet, and occasional sunfish.

The catching of fish by white pelicans is a community affair. When a school is detected in shallow water the discovering pelicans herd the fish toward shore by beating their wings and treading their web feet on the muddy bottom. This activity draws more birds and as the flock grows it forms into a semicircle, pushing the fish shoreward. As dorsal fins and tails begin to show on the surface, the beaks of the birds probe the mud, roiling the water still more and obliterating all avenues of escape to deeper and safer portions of the Salton Sea. Still in a community movement, the birds tighten the circle and drive their prey into water so shallow that it no longer conceals. Then the luckless fish are scooped up, swallowed, and later regurgitated to the young waiting on the islands nearby.

YOUNG MOUNTAIN SHEEP. The young of the mountain sheep are ready to take care of themselves soon after birth. *L. W. Walker*

WEASEL (*Mustela frenata*). In spite of its size, the weasel is a dauntless, ferocious fighter. Length: about 16 inches. *L. W. Walker.*

The Mammals of the Southwest

BY LEWIS WAYNE WALKER

FOR MANY THOUSANDS of years man and the other mammals of the Southwest were compatible. The aborigines took what they needed for food, and natural reproduction filled the gaps. As primitive methods of hunting slowly improved, the prey was given time to adjust and man was like a present-day predator, eliminating the aged and sick. Parts of the country must have resembled the veldts of Africa, not necessarily in variety of species but certainly in the population of individuals.

Then our European ancestors penetrated the West with their startling weapons, ingenious traps and deadly poisons, and in several hundred years exterminated perhaps more animals than had been forever lost on all the other continents of the world. It's a sorry record, a permanent blot, but perhaps it was necessary in order to show that such populations, despite their numbers, are not inexhaustible. Perhaps it was the necessary incentive to conservation — a conservation which is now commencing to bring back some of the species thought to be hopelessly gone.

Along the shores of the Pacific, eastward to the Mississippi, north to Canada, and south to central Mexico was the rough former range of the coyotes. Early histories pictured these desert wolves as furtive animals, not extremely courageous and perfectly satisfied to live on the dead and dying members of the tremendous herds of hoofed animals which cattle eventually replaced. When rabbits or other small mammals were available they

KIT FOX (*Vulpes velox*). The kit fox is capable of great speed. It hunts at night for mice and rats and lives in an underground burrow. Length: less than 36 inches. *U.S. Fish & Wildlife Service*

supplied fresh meat, but in general the coyotes were scavengers content to live on carrion even though they were capable of destroying aged or sick mammals many times their size. In destruction of the latter they were performing a most necessary function: stopping the spread of epidemics with the effective quarantine of death.

As sluggish domesticated stock gradually replaced fleet wild animals, the bolder coyotes of that day reaped a harvest. The new creatures introduced by man were easy prey and to coyotes their capture was no more arduous than the picking off of the diseased of the native herds. Guns, traps, poisons, and snares were all brought to bear on the so-called "varmints" and although many succumbed to the campaign of killing many also survived. Each generation of survivors seemed to breed super-intelligence into the pups and despite this greatest hunt in history that typically western sound, the staccato bark of coyotes, has never been silenced.

All during this campaign a similar one was being waged on timber wolves of the high mountains and of the far north until they were practically exterminated from areas where they were formerly common. This destruction left gaps where a certain population of predators was necessary. Coyotes filled the bill. Their static range suddenly expanded in a movement that has not yet been stopped. From their time-honored home in the

GRAY FOX (*Urocyon*). The gray fox is the only member of the fox family that can climb trees. Length: about 42 inches from nose to tail. *U.S. Fish & Wildlife Service*

southwestern states the prairie wolf or coyote has gone east to the Atlantic and north to the Arctic Sea in the most rapid voluntary range expansion ever known to occur with any one species of wild animal.

Since those early days when the mere mention of coyotes practically coincided with the reach for a rifle there has been a decided change in both four-legged fugitive and human hunter. Individual coyotes which could not resist stock are now almost memories of the past. Their sly descendants have almost given up carrion-eating as too dangerous and have switched their attention to rabbits and other small animals. As a result many of the ranchers are changing their opinions in regard to this predator and are beginning to view coyotes as allies instead of enemies. One association of cattlemen which controls an area about five hundred miles long and two hundred wide has passed resolutions condemning the indiscriminate poisoning and trapping of coyotes on any of the property which the association controls. Their reason for the about-face is based on the theory of natural balance, which the ranchers had to learn the expensive way. Whenever coyote-poisoners worked ranching territory in the past, the next several years produced plagues of rabbits; and rodent poisons or costly rabbit drives were then necessary.

There is an old story here in the Southwest about a pair of rabbits being chased by hounds.

BIGHORN SHEEP (*Ovis canadensis*), Kofa Game Range, Yuma, Arizona. A fully-grown bighorn may average forty inches in shoulder height and range in weight from 175 to 350 pounds. They range from southern British Columbia to northwestern Chihuahua, Mexico. Length: 6 feet, Height: 3 feet, Weight: 225 lbs. *U.S. Fish & Wildlife Service*

WILD BURRO (*Equus asinus*) on the range. The burro, a very small member of the donkey family, is a patient and long-suffering creature. In the development of the Southwest, it did its share in carrying heavy burdens. *U.S. Fish & Wildlife Service*

Such pursuits are not unusual. As the story goes, this pair lived up to its reputation, stopped for a moment, and then outnumbered the dogs. Slow the story down a bit and it could almost be the truth, for rabbits—from the diminutive brush variety of the Pacific Coast to the antelope jacks of Arizona, New Mexico, and Colorado—are subject to rapid changes in population. Cottontails breed at an age of four or five months and have about four litters a year of from three to five young. The first-born offspring produce before the season ends, hence it is possible to get three generations in a single year. This pyramiding process multiplies rapidly and might be likened to the daily doubling of money from the start of only one penny on the beginning day. There is no bank in the world that could stand the drain for more than a few months; and if the same thing were to occur in rabbits the entire produce of a country would be stripped in six or seven rabbit generations.

However, the above is theory. Such production has never occurred and probably never will, although Australia's introduced rabbits, without predatory animals to control them, threatened for many years. Here in the Southwest, rabbits are food for just about every predatory mammal from bears on down to tiny weasels, and they are also food for many reptiles and birds. This is a vast army of prevention. Some of these predators are

LONGHORN STEER, one of a vanishing breed on the Wichita National Wildlife Refuge, Oklahoma. *U.S. Fish & Wildlife Service*

stationary and as long as they exist in sufficient numbers the area remains in balance. Others are roving, enticed to areas where food is abundant, but quick to move on whenever it becomes scarce. As a result there are seasonal fluctuations with both grass-eaters and meat-eaters.

All too often an over-abundance of either brings on a campaign of extermination, and if some of the modern poisons are used the results are disastrous. The lethal 1080 is one of the meanest of the poison mixtures, due to its chain reaction. If set for predatory animals it is usually placed in a carcass or inserted in a bait of meat and any hungry animal that eats it crawls off and dies. Then his carcass becomes lethal and passes killing power to the numerous predators that augment their diet with occasional carrion.

This wholesale slaughter of predators gives the rabbits, gophers, mice and ground squirrels, which had been reduced by the predatory animals, a chance to recoup at a much faster rate than could normally be expected. Then calls go out for poison grain. And again, each creature that partakes and later is caught by predators kills another animal which, if left alive, could help the situation. In the past few years many states have strictly curtailed the use of poison as a control for wild animals. Most naturalists feel that such legislation is a forward step in conservation.

Imagine, if you can, a city about 750 miles long

BLACK BEAR (*Euarctos americanus*) is found in many of the wooded areas of North America and in the plateau region of Mexico. Length: 6 feet, Height: 3 feet, Weight: 300 lbs. *U.S. Fish & Wildlife Service*

BLACK BEAR AND CUBS, Yellowstone Park, Wyoming. Tourists would do well to enjoy bears from a safe distance when in parks. Length: to 6 ft., Height: 3 ft., Weight: 300 lbs. *U.S. Fish & Wildlife Service*

AMERICAN BISON (*Bison bison*) in House Rock Valley. The American bison once roamed the plains in vast herds that may have numbered four million. Height: 5 to 6 feet, Weight: 1 ton. *Union Pacific Railroad*

and 200 wide, with an inhabitant every 15 or 20 feet. This is the rumored size of a prairie dog colony which existed in Texas in the pioneer days. Now, however, it has been bisected by roads and dotted by the cities and towns of humans. There are only a few spots in the entire area where prairie dogs still exist, but even though the animals are gone the ancient colony is supplying interesting data on the habitations of these unique social rodents.

In excavations for skyscrapers on this land formerly controlled by the dogs, the sheer walls show faint tracings of ancient tunnels. These are completely filled in with a soil that was formerly surface dirt but has been carried deep underground by rains. In most instances the extreme depth of the tunnels is about 20 feet, and at about 15 feet the ground is crisscrossed with a maze of horizontal burrows.

Most of the surface entrances drop almost vertically, and about two feet below the ground level there are signs of a small side pocket. This was the barking platform where a dog, hard pressed by an enemy, would hesitate and bark a warning to underground members of the colony.

The rumored story that prairie dog tunnels go to underground water tables has not been vindicated by the Texas excavations, but research is

BIGHORN SHEEP (*Ovis canadensis*) on the range near Yuma, Arizona. The bighorn, although its coat is hairy rather than woolly, is a true sheep. There are nine geographical varieties. This one is the desert mountain sheep. Length: 6 feet, Height: 3 feet, Weight: 225 lbs. *U.S. Fish & Wildlife Service*

TWO MULE DEER BUCKS (*Odocoileus hemionus*) on the National Bison Range, Moiese, Montana. They are called mule deer because of their long ears. Length: 6 feet, Height: 4 feet, Weight: 350 lbs. *U.S. Fish & Wildlife Service*

being carried on relative to water absorption by the tunnels. Dirt displacement is also being studied. The findings might belatedly prove, now that prairie dogs are on the verge of extinction, that they were not such bad citizens after all.

Visualize the water storage capacity of the millions of miles contained in these six-inch tubular tunnels and imagine water underground where evaporation is held to a minimum, and where there is slow seepage to the underground water tables. At present, hidden underground reservoirs are being taxed far beyond their capacities to refill and in all parts of the West underground water levels are rapidly lowering. Visualize also the sterile dirt removed by the dogs from deep underground, and carried to the surface to be energized by the sun, then carried underground again to fill the burrows in a harmless erosion which simply added depth to existing topsoil. Although the dogs are almost gone, destroyed as unnecessary pests, perhaps in time their worth will be known.

There are several animals of the Southwest which are almost legendary, due to their rarity. One of these, the black-footed ferret, was a parasite of prairie dogs when the latter existed in countless millions. This ferret is truly a mystery animal, with its closest relative a native of Siberia. Despite all the human travel, trapping, and explorations prior

WHITE-TAILED DEER (*Odocoileus virginianus*). The white-tailed deer ranges over much of the United States, Canada, and Mexico. Length: 5 feet, Height: 3 feet, Weight: 250 lbs. *U.S. Fish & Wildlife Service*

to 1850 the black-footed ferret remained unknown until 1851 when it was described by Audubon on the basis of an imperfect skin. Many more years passed and it remained unseen. Some naturalists of the late nineteenth century openly scoffed at the previous record and termed it a fake. Then a few more skins cropped up. At the present time there are only about one hundred specimens in the collections of the world and with the extinction of prairie dogs well on the way this ferret is bound to go also. Practically nothing is known of its habits and although its range, at least the northern part, seems to have been east of the Continental Divide there are a few sight records which also

PRONGHORN ANTELOPE (*Antilocapra americana*), Desert Game Range, near Las Vegas, Nevada. The pronghorn is not a true antelope nor is it a deer. Scientifically, it belongs to a family all to itself. This female has no characteristic pronged horns. Length: 5 feet, Shoulder Height: 3 feet, Weight: 110 lbs. *U.S. Fish & Wildlife Service*

BLACK-FOOTED FERRET (*Mustela nigripes*). The black-footed ferret is on the road to extinction since it depends on the prairie dog for its food. Length of body: up to 18 inches, Length of tail: 6 inches. *U.S. Fish & Wildlife Service*

place its existence in the prairie dog towns of Arizona.

Buffalos and the western plains will forever be linked together, and their teeming millions were the mammalian counterpart of the millions of passenger pigeons which formerly frequented the eastern states. The latter however are gone and but for action in the nick of time the buffalo would have suffered the same fate. Most reliable estimates settle on a figure of 60 million animals in the buffalo's heyday, when they ranged from Canada to central Texas. That was during the period when the early scouts were probing the West, supplying Indians with more efficient methods of killing, and in general proceeding along the lines which no doubt were even then called progress.

By 1800 the number of buffalos had dropped to 40 million and by 1850 to one-third of their all-time high. Then the slaughter accelerated at a

PRONGHORN ANTELOPE (*Antilocapra americana*). The pronghorn resembles an antelope but does not belong to the antelope family but to one all its own! This one is at the Desert Game Range, Las Vegas, Nevada. Length: 5 feet, Shoulder Height: 3 feet. Weight: 110 lbs. *U.S. Fish & Wildlife Service*

speed that was unbelievable. By the end of the century less than one thousand animals were left. Action to prevent complete extermination was taken just in time; and at present the buffalos' numbers are in excess of twenty-five thousand and the future of the species is assured.

Several other big game animals of the Southwest have suffered similar fates. One of these, the desert mountain sheep, has even been forced to change habits in order that the meager remnant of former numbers might remain alive. The early explorers, crossing the deserts, found these wonderful sheep abundant on the flats. The banks of the Gila, the Santa Cruz, and the Colorado rivers were crisscrossed by their tracks; and their flesh was the most easily procured meat in desert regions. Some of the stage stations had piles of sheep horns stacked to three times the height of a man — piles so big that in order to duplicate them now all the sheep of any southwestern state would have to be killed.

But from an estimated half million in the early days of the Southwest's occupation, the sheep population of Arizona, California, New Mexico, and Nevada dropped so low that the animals were often rumored to be extinct. These sheep that liked

DESERT MOUNTAIN SHEEP, Kofa Game Range, Yuma, Arizona. *U.S. Fish & Wildlife Service*

BUCK AND DOE MULE DEER at waterhole in the desert.
Length: 6 feet, Height: 4 feet, Weight: 350 lbs. *L. W. Walker*

to nibble grasses along the rivers were easy prey and before long only a few bands were left on the inaccessible parts of the range. To survive, these modified their way of life, forsaking waterholes during daylight hours and in general shunning lowland valleys. Today's survivors owe their existence to a few individual families which held to inaccessible crags. Their population has now climbed to ten or fifteen thousand.

As individuals, these sheep are peculiar and entirely unpredictable. In almost all recent literature, much of it obviously fiction, they are pictured as sagacious and crafty, extremely difficult to approach, and knowing every trick of the trade to escape detection. However, in my experiences with them, stretching over the past twenty years both in the States and in Baja California, I have found them ridiculously easy to approach, not un-

CALIFORNIA MULE DEER, Yosemite National Park, California, bedded down. Length: 6 feet, Shoulder Height: 4 feet, Weight: 350 lbs. *National Park Service*

necessarily wary, and readily fooled into making an appearance when their curiosity is aroused. One trick that I have seen Mexican hunters use on the east side of the mountains south of Imperial Valley, California, seems infallible when sheep are in that region. These mountains rise from about sea level to 6,000 feet. They are stepped with numerous ledges and are almost sheer where they join the floor of the sedimentary valley below. A road used by wood-cutters runs along the base.

On one of my trips into this lonely area to photograph kit fox, I was disturbed by a baffling noise, rapidly approaching from the south. It sounded like a tin shop being ransacked and the sound was magnified by echoes from rock wall to rock wall. Then around the bend came a wood-cutter's truck, with two men standing in the back, high-powered rifles in readiness. Roped on the

AMERICAN BISON (*Bison bison*). The American bison or plains buffalo once roamed the plains in herds as large as 4 million. Today they are far from extinct and they are numbered in the thousands. Length: 10 feet, Height: 6 feet. *U.S. Fish & Wildlife Service*

rear of the truck was a motley collection of dented gas cans and oil drums. These were being dragged over the rocks to create a terrific din. Upon questioning the driver, I learned that this was the customary way to procure mountain sheep as food for the wood-cutter camps. The system was successful due to the extreme curiosity of the prey.

The first few trips along the base of the cliff were usually unproductive and sometimes the hunters would even see the sheep scamper to higher ground, well out of range. In time, however, fear of the noise—which was evidently harmless—would be overcome by a questioning "What is it?" The sheep that ran a short time before would descend from the higher cliffs and actually lean over the edge in an effort to fathom the commotion, forming ideal targets.

The kit fox that drew me to this region of mountain sheep were once common from central Mexico to the Canadian border, but became depleted when coyote poisoning was popular. Naturally the varied habitats throughout the western states developed many local races, but the one best known and still existing in limited numbers is a pale-colored creature which dwells on or near sand dunes. These foxes, along with horned toads and desert sidewinders, are prize examples of parallel evolution. Each has an unrelated counterpart on the deserts of some other continent; the fox has the fennic of Africa, the horned toad has the moloch of Australia, and the sidewinder has the horned viper of the Sahara.

A few years ago on a field trip I had an interesting experience with kit fox. Ten rattlesnakes and one non-poisonous racer had been captured. Each was placed in a cloth sack and the bags were then piled under my cot in the shade. Kit fox were constant visitors around the camp and, as is their nature when they are not molested, they had tamed rapidly. Some even took food from my fingers and at night sniffed over every inch of ground for the tiny scraps of food that were dropped. At the termination of my stay I counted the sacks and found one missing. It was the sack that contained the harmless reptile. This snake could not have gone off by itself without leaving the sack behind, and the only conclusion that can be drawn is that the inquisitive kits, nosing about, pushed the dangerous reptiles aside and picked the only one of the eleven that was harmless.

The gray fox, only other member of the family found in the southwestern states, is entirely unlike the diminutive kits which have such trusting natures. This larger relative is a furtive species which rarely permits close approach and, according to available information, is the only member of the entire family that habitually climbs trees. On several occasions I have encountered gray foxes in small paloverdes, ten or twelve feet from the ground. When discovered, they run down the trunks head first. They are not at all particular in choice of food and seem to show an equal

AMERICAN BISON COWS with calves at the Wichita Wildlife Refuge near Cache, Oklahoma. Height: 5 to 6 feet, Weight: 1 ton. *U.S. Fish & Wildlife Service*

THE PRAIRIE DOG (*Cynomys*) built underground "cities" with miles of tunnels and dens extending in all directions. Today, the little prairie dog has all but vanished from the Western scene. Length: 14 to 17 inches. *U.S. Fish & Wildlife Service*

AMERICAN BADGER (*Taxidea*). The American badger, shown in the Desert Game Range, Las Vegas, Nevada, can dig itself out of sight in a matter of seconds. Length: 2 feet, Weight: 20 lbs. *U.S. Fish & Wildlife Service*

PECCARY (*Tagassu tajacu*) seen at the Aransas Refuge, Austwell, Texas, is also called javeline or musk hog. They are the only piglike animals native to America but are not true pigs. Length: 38 inches. *U.S. Fish & Wildlife Service*

PRAIRIE DOG at its burrow. This little animal is not a dog but a ground squirrel and is as much a part of the West as is the Indian. Length: 14 to 17 inches. *Photo by L. W. Walker*

fondness for both vegetable and animal matter.

The southern deserts of the border states (Arizona to Texas) are habitats preferred by America's only native pigs, the peccaries, and in some sections of their range they are still comparatively common. These are peculiar animals with short legs, stocky bodies, and heads that seem about a size too large. A few inches above an absurdly short tail they have a well-developed musk sac which is used to spread a scent and keep the herd in contact. Tucson's Desert Museum has many peccaries in the area and we have often observed herds progressing from nearby valleys to our photographic waterhole. As each adult animal passes under a branch, its back arches to scrape the musk gland on the bark. Other animals which follow do not ostentatiously notice such spots, but their choice of the same track is seemingly more than just coincidence.

Most of the peccaries' foraging is done at night, but their daytime feeding in strictly protected areas leads me to believe that nocturnal activity is an acquired characteristic due to the pressure of hunting. Where they are considered game animals they usually rest in compact groups during the heat of the day, and their coarse gray hair makes them inconspicuous against nearby boulders. Their sight and possibly hearing are not well developed and these sleeping groups are often surprised by hunters

COYOTE (*Canis latrans*) is the voice of the West. Its complicated repertory of barks, yips, whines, howls, and cries carries a long way on the evening desert air. Length: to 3 ft. *U.S. Fish & Wildlife Service*

RINGTAILED CAT (*Bassariscus*) is a shy animal but a great catcher of rats and mice. Length: 28 inches. *U.S. Fish & Wildlife Service*

or hikers. The reaction of peccaries to a sudden disturbance is similar to the sudden flushing of a covey of quail. They literally explode to all points of the compass, each animal grunting and gnashing its tusks and running in the direction it had faced when startled. A few of the group run toward the danger instead of away from it and that seems to be the basis for the often-heard story of attacks by wild pigs.

The staff of the Desert Museum has checked many stories of attacks which have supposedly occurred in Tucson Mountain Park. In every case, the person "attacked" has emerged unharmed as far as peccary damage is concerned, although some persons have come out badly scratched from trying to climb cactus or other spiny growth. For short distances the wild pigs are extremely fast and if an attack was intentional it is very doubtful that a person could evade the first rush.

Another story about peccaries credits them, and deer, with the ability and desire to kill every rattlesnake encountered. The Museum photographic blind has enabled the staff to check these rumors thoroughly and they, like the "attacks," seem groundless.

Every three months for over a year rattlesnakes, milked of their venom, were tethered just beyond the waterhole on a game trail used by about fifty animals a night. After a few struggles to escape, the tethered snake usually calmed and reposed quietly. Soon after dark the crunching of hoofs on gravel warned us, only ten feet away, that animals were approaching. Even though snakes are deaf they pick up ground vibrations, and these tied reptiles proved that point by more struggles when the deer or peccaries were still not in sight. Finally from out of the darkness an animal would appear and with hesitant steps would approach the water. If the snake moved at this time he was instantly noticed and the thirsty creature, either pig or deer, would sometimes bolt into the darkness again. However, in every case, the fright was only momentary and within a few moments the mammal, followed by others, would approach once more. Then the bravest of the lot would step over the reptile and drink, and others would crowd behind. On several occasions the snake struck the deer or pigs which touched his body with their hoofs, but they never made any attempt to retaliate by trampling him into the ground.

These waterhole observations have afforded scientists an unequaled opportunity to view many desert animals at extremely close range. Throughout a normal evening during the dry seasons mule deer are sure visitors, and then in the order of numerical appearance come the skunks — hooded, spotted, hog-nosed, and striped. Next most common are the peccaries, followed by foxes, badgers, ring-tailed cats, coyotes, pack rats, and rarely raccoons. The last four animals appear only when all other visitors are out of sight and hearing. The others have a strange chain of command seemingly controlled by the prowess of their weapons, even though the rattlers, most deadly of all, are sometimes practically ignored.

When deer are drinking and are disturbed by foxes or badgers, they usually make short rushes at the newcomers. The visiting foxes will always retreat and then wait, 20 or 30 feet away, for the pool to become less crowded. Some badgers act in a similar way, but there have been times when one will stand his ground; and then the deer will back off. Until the first animals at the pool finish drinking, the two species exist under an armed truce. Every animal visitor retreats when the peccaries arrive. When these pig herds number several scores their approach is forecast by rattling stones and a musky odor which permeates the countryside.

HOG-NOSED SKUNK (*Conepatus*). This large animal digs with its nose in the ground to find the insects which make up a good part of its diet. Length: to 28 inches. *L. W. Walker*

Skunks, however, really rule the roost. Deer, peccaries, and all the others usually treat them with an awesome respect. The large animals seem fully aware that the weapon skunks use is a long-range one, and one that can temporarily blind and can make an animal disliked for many days even by his own kind. Though armed with this powerful weapon, the skunks are really gentlemen and despite good provocation, according to waterhole observers, withhold spraying until bluffs and threats have proved to be failures. Actually this reluctance to do damage is a characteristic of most North American mammals. They live and let live, and kill when compelled by hunger and not for sport.

RACCOON (*Procyon*). Raccoons have long, sensitive fingers, can open almost any fastening, and are delightful but mischievous animals. Length: 30 inches. *U.S. Fish & Wildlife Service*

Index

CREATED AND PRODUCED
BY
BOOKSERVICE AMERICA